Grazing Management Planning for Upland Natura 2000 Sites: A Practical Manual

Fiona E. Stewart
and Sarah G. Eno

Published 1998

ISBN 0 901625 604

Designed and typeset by
Harry Scott, Pica Design

Illustrated by
Craig Ellery, 10 Cheyne Walk, Stockbridge, Edinburgh EH4 1JE

Edited by
Sylvia Sullivan

Printed by
Xpress Print, Aberdeen

Published by
The National Trust for Scotland

Front cover:
Beinn Fhada & Gearr Aonach with cloud hovering on Bidean nam Bian (*James Fenton*)

Front cover inset:
Sheep grazing on heather moor - the 'fence-line' effect (*James Fenton*)

Back cover inset:
Saxifraga azoides - a typical flowering plant of high altitude flushes (*Kath Lee*)

Grazing Management Planning for Upland Natura 2000 Sites

Contents

Appendices

References and Further Reading   **142**

Foreword

Copies of this manual and the case study grazing plans may be obtained from the following:

James Fenton, NTS, The Old Granary, West Mill Street, Perth, PH1 5QP

Helen Armstrong, Uplands Group, SNH, 2 Anderson Place, Edinburgh, EH6 5NP

This manual is the main output from a European Union LIFE funded project on Upland Grazing. The work was headed by The National Trust for Scotland in partnership with Scottish Natural Heritage, Institute of Terrestrial Ecology, Scottish Wildlife Trust and Macaulay Land Use Research Institute.

A project team was set up in January 1996 and started designing a draft methodology for grazing management plans for upland Special Areas of Conservation in Scotland. The methodology was tested for four Scottish candidate SACs and the experience and knowledge so gained is now brought together in this manual.

Throughout the project the team have been constantly modifying and updating their approach in accordance with the developments taking place in this field of work. As we write, the Joint Nature Conservancy Council, the country agencies and other LIFE projects are developing guidelines, protocols and common terminology to aid the conservation and management of features of interest located on designated sites in Britain. As this work becomes available, it should help with some of the processes identified in this manual.

Management plan structure and content will always be evolving in response to changes in legislation, policies and priorities. We therefore expect that future work will be able to build on what we have done, in the way that we too have built on past efforts.

We welcome feedback and comments which will help in revising and updating future versions of the manual. Please use the Feedback form enclosed.

Good Luck!

Sarah Eno, Project Leader
Fiona Stewart, Project Officer
Fiona Maclachlan, Project Administration Manager
EU Life Upland Grazing Team, March 1998

Acknowledgements

We would like to thank the many people who gave freely of their time to discuss, clarify and comment on this manual. They are too numerous to mention all by name, but some deserve particular attention. The steering group for the project consisted of James Fenton of The National Trust for Scotland, Helen Armstrong of Scottish Natural Heritage, David Welch of Institute of Terrestrial Ecology, Neil Willcox of Scottish Wildlife Trust and John Milne of Macaulay Land Use Research Institute; their advice (inevitably conflicting at times), encouragement and criticism has been there throughout the development of the manual. Roy A. Harris, nature conservation management consultant, helped find a niche for the manual, advised on sheep management and kept our feet on the ground. The delegates who attended the project workshop where the manual underwent a major review were generous in their contributions. The following individuals have commented on the manual and appendices; Sandy MacLennan, Phil Shaw, Angus MacDonald, Daniel Gotts (all of Scottish Natural Heritage), Marcus Yeo of Countryside Council for Wales and Joanne Backshall of English Nature. Andrew Bachell and Ian Cunningham (of The National Trust for Scotland) commented on the final draft. Thanks also to people who wrote appendices, where they are mentioned by name. Many thanks too, to the illustrator, Craig Ellery, to the manual designer, Harry Scott and to Sylvia Sullivan our editor, who were patient and responsive to our demands.

Besides the manual, the project has also had help from many people in the development of the grazing management plans. These people are acknowledged in the relevant site plan. As a LIFE project, liaison with Europe has been essential and many thanks go to Ian Hepburn of Ecosystems. The project team also said goodbye to Kath Lee the earlier Project Leader, who left to have a baby and Ann Tourney, Project Administration Manager, who moved to Australia.

FEEDBACK FORM

Name

Position

Name of Organisation

Contact Address

Telephone

If you have used the
Manual for management
planning, how could it be
made more appropriate
to your needs:

PLEASE SEND YOUR
COMPLETED FORMS TO:

Helen Armstrong,
Uplands Group,
Advisory Services,
Scottish Natural Heritage,
2 Anderson Place,
Edinburgh EH6 5NP.

A. Introduction to the Manual; its Purpose and Aims

Purpose

This manual provides guidance on the preparation of grazing plans for Natura 2000 sites in the uplands of the European Community. It is based on the experience gained from writing grazing plans for four case study Special Areas for Conservation (SACs) in Scotland and so focuses particularly on SACs, but the principles may be applied to any upland site where nature conservation is an objective. The manual is intended to be used by anyone writing a grazing plan for such sites, although it is assumed that users will have some understanding of the impacts of grazing on vegetation, a knowledge of plant communities and/or experience of management planning. For this reason, the manual is designed to be a reference source to be dipped into as required.

Grazing can have both positive and negative impacts on features of nature conservation value. It may be desirable to eliminate existing grazing completely, or grazing may be used as a tool in order to meet objectives. Grazing is manipulated via the management of herbivores, usually large herbivores and this manual describes a process for determining the most appropriate management.

Aims

The manual aims to assist the user in the preparation of grazing plans in four ways:

- It proposes a structure for grazing plans in terms of a series of plan components. The structure is designed to be applicable to a range of sites.

- It describes the preparation of each component of the grazing plan, describing the information required at each stage, how to use it and where such information may be obtained.

- It leads the user through the decision-making process, describing how information should be used to reach conclusions about the best grazing management for a site.

- It provides, in the appendices, a source of detailed information on specific topics of particular relevance to sites in Scotland, in some cases, Great Britain, or even more widely.

B. How to Use the Manual

Following the introductory sections (A, B and C) this manual consists of:

- main text providing guidance on the preparation of grazing plans; divided into Parts 1 and 2

- appendices providing detailed information on a selected range of subjects of use for grazing plans; with particular reference to Scotland

- a reference list and Bibliography

About the Manual

The text in Parts 1 and 2 of the manual is sub-divided into components numbered 1.1, 1.2... 2.1, 2.2 etc. which correspond with the main components of a grazing plan. A specimen table of contents for a grazing plan, showing the sub-sections of a plan, is given in Example box 1. The manual provides guidance on the preparation of each plan component and is designed to be a reference source so that users may access individual components. Before proceeding, read section C 'The Structure of Grazing Plans' which describes the plan format presented in this manual.

Within Parts 1 and 2 of the manual, there are key elements which are used to aid interpretation:

- Extracts from four case study grazing plans are given as worked examples of some of the processes described in the manual. These case studies are presented at the end of the relevant component in the manual.

- Short examples of points made in the manual are shown in 'Example' boxes, numbered 1, 2 etc.

- Explanatory text which describes terms used in the manual or gives detailed information on an aspect of the process is presented in 'Information' boxes, numbered 1, 2 etc.

- A figure illustrating the order of the main plan components is shown on each page of Parts 1 and 2, highlighted to indicate the location of the component to which the page refers.

- Flow charts are used to illustrate particularly complicated processes.

Getting Through The Planning Process

TACKLING THE PLANNING PROCESS USING THIS MANUAL

Read sections A, B, C
↓
Collate descriptive information as discussed in Part 1
↓
Decide on the policy and select key features as described in 2.1, 2.2
↓
Write the objectives for the key features, as described in 2.3
↓
Work through the decision-making process as described in 2.5
↓
Start to write the plan

The manual suggests a way of presenting information in a grazing plan, but the plan need not be prepared and written in this order because planning is an iterative process. A guide to the tasks involved in preparing a grazing plan using this manual is shown in the box 'Tackling the Planning Process Using This Manual'.

C. The Grazing Plan Structure

The format for the case study plans was originally based on the approach described by the Countryside Council for Wales (CCW) in 'A Guide to the Production of Management Plans for Nature Reserves and Protected Areas' (CCW, 1996). The structure described here results from changes to the CCW format, made where necessary for grazing-specific plans and to resolve problems encountered during the planning process.

The grazing plan is divided into two parts:
- Part 1; 'Introduction and Description'

- Part 2; 'Objectives and Management'

These two parts can be arranged in reverse order if preferred, but the Introduction should always be included at the start of the plan. Parts 1 and 2 are sub-divided into components as shown in Figure 1. This figure is repeated on each page to show what part of the plan the page refers to.

Management plans generally include a **Description** and in grazing plans this contains information directly relevant to grazing. The planning format is based on a set of **key features**. These are the features at which management is aimed, and in grazing plans, they will normally be plant species, animal species or plant communities. The key features are a sub-set of the total range of biological features at a site, selected because they have particular conservation value. The selection of the key features is based on the range of **obligations and policies** for the site and is described in **'Selection and Evaluation of Key Features'**. This is an important step because it is the key features which drive the management decisions made. Specific **objectives** are written for individual key features, defining requirements in terms of measurable attributes, which can be monitored as a means of determining whether objectives are being met.

For each key feature, the **current condition** must be assessed as an indicator of whether a change to the current management is required. Through the discussion of the **impacts of grazing** on individual key features, an ideal grazing pattern is determined for each. Following this, the factors which control the opportunities for implementing any of the ideal grazing patterns are identified and described. These are referred to as **factors which influence the management of the features** (factors); often called 'opportunities and constraints' in other management plan formats. To produce realistic proposals for grazing management, the ideal grazing patterns for the various key features are compared and a regime that meets the objectives at a site level, rather than feature level, has to be selected.

The options for attaining this grazing pattern depend on the management of herbivores and the practicalities of implementing such management. These issues are discussed with a view to making firm proposals for management in the **'Rationale and Recommendations for Grazing Management'**.

Monitoring is an essential part of grazing plans because the management of grazing is not an exact science; the relationships between grazing pressure and habitat condition and between animal densities and grazing pressure are poorly understood. As a result, recommendations for grazing management may amount to a best guess, and it will be essential to determine whether the grazing regime produces the required results, in terms of objectives, or if it needs to be changed. This monitoring will be based on the set of attributes used to define the objectives, but it is unlikely to be feasible to measure all the attributes of each feature, due to limited resources. This means that the priorities for **monitoring projects** need to be identified. A full summary of the recommended grazing regime, the monitoring priorities and any other work projects identified in the plan are listed as a set of **prescriptions** for the site, along with the objectives to which each prescription, project or recommendation applies.

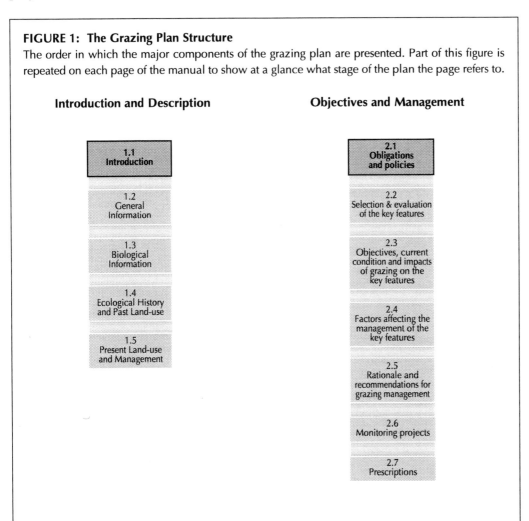

FIGURE 1: The Grazing Plan Structure
The order in which the major components of the grazing plan are presented. Part of this figure is repeated on each page of the manual to show at a glance what stage of the plan the page refers to.

Introduction and Description

- 1.1 Introduction
- 1.2 General Information
- 1.3 Biological Information
- 1.4 Ecological History and Past Land-use
- 1.5 Present Land-use and Management

Objectives and Management

- 2.1 Obligations and policies
- 2.2 Selection & evaluation of the key features
- 2.3 Objectives, current condition and impacts of grazing on the key features
- 2.4 Factors affecting the management of the key features
- 2.5 Rationale and recommendations for grazing management
- 2.6 Monitoring projects
- 2.7 Prescriptions

Integrating Grazing Plans with Wider Site Plans

In addition to the management of grazing, there may be other planning issues at a site, such as recreation. The relationship between grazing and these issues varies between sites and is not dealt with in detail here. A management plan that deals with other aspects of site management may be written separately to the grazing plan, or as part of the same plan. In either case, the principles described here can be used to select a grazing regime for the site. If the grazing plan is prepared separately, it may be necessary to integrate it with other plans. This will have implications for the grazing plan, both for its content and its structure. It may be necessary to produce a grazing plan that differs in format from the layout proposed here, but this manual may still be used for guidance on content.

WRITING THE GRAZING PLAN

Part 1
INTRODUCTION AND DESCRIPTION

Part 1 of this manual describes the Introduction and Description for a grazing plan. The plan should always start with an Introduction that summarises its purpose. The Description includes summarised background information and detailed information which is used to help make decisions about grazing management.

The subjects for inclusion in the Description are discussed in this manual in the order they appear in the grazing plan. Possible sources of information are suggested for each component. Some refer specifically to Britain, although in practice, many sources are generic and will apply to the rest of the EU.

The level of detail provided on each subject will depend on its relevance to grazing management. A grazing plan should focus on the characteristics important to grazing management; background information about the site can be presented briefly, whilst information used in the decision-making process should be detailed. There are no straightforward rules on how much detail to include in the Description but the manual highlights the points to consider when selecting information for inclusion. For guidance on the preparation of a more full description, refer to general planning guides e.g. CCW (1996) or NCC (1988).

1.1 Introduction

● *summarises the purpose of the plan*

● *explains the plan content; e.g. grazing only or grazing and recreation*

Content and Purpose

The Introduction is required to give readers basic information about the grazing plan. First of all, the Introduction should describe the purpose of the plan; for example, if it deals only with the management of grazing for the conservation of SAC features on the site, this should be stated. The Introduction should also state whether the plan is integrated with another, wider site management plan, or whether it is the only plan for the site. If the grazing plan is integrated with another, indicate the allocation of information between the plans; particularly the descriptive information.

EXAMPLE BOX 2: Introduction to the Ben Lawers cSAC Grazing Plan

This grazing plan deals with the management of sheep and deer on the Ben Lawers candidate Special Area for Conservation (cSAC). It will ultimately be integrated into a wider site management plan, which is currently being developed. A management statement for the Ben Lawers Site of Special Scientific Interest is being prepared by Scottish Natural Heritage (SNH), and The National Trust for Scotland (NTS) is currently developing a plan for the parts of the Ben Lawers National Nature Reserve in its ownership. In the past, full management plans have been produced for the Ben Lawers National Nature Reserve (NNR) and the most recent version of that plan is entitled 'Ben Lawers National Nature Reserve Third Management Plan 1993-1997'. For this grazing plan, general site aims and basic site information have been summarised from the 1993-1997 draft of the NNR plan and the SSSI notification documents. Species information therefore applies either to the SSSI or the NNR, the boundaries of which are shown in Map 1.

Grazing management is aimed primarily at the cSAC features, which are habitats listed in Annex I of the Habitats and Species Directive. These include both 'qualifying' and 'occurring' Annex I habitats, although priority is given to 'qualifying' habitats. 'Qualifying' habitats are those Annex I habitats for which Ben Lawers was selected as a cSAC, because these are particularly well represented at the site, in comparison to other sites in the UK. 'Occurring' habitats are other Annex I habitats present at the site. The site supports several nationally rare higher plant species and these have also been considered in the process of determining grazing management prescriptions.

1.2 General Information

- summarised basic site information

- the physical character of the site

- non-biological features of interest

Purpose

It is very useful in any management plan to set the scene and describe the character of the site. Much of the general site information is not directly relevant to grazing and so can be summarised in a grazing plan, but there will be some variation between sites. Decisions about how much detail to include need to be made for individual sites, but some points to consider are described here.

Content

This section should include the following subjects:

■ site location and tenure (ownership)

■ physical characteristics

■ designations

■ historical and archaeological interest

■ landscape and cultural value

Site Location and Tenure

Indicate the location of your site clearly, using grid references and maps. Basic details of tenure, (site ownership) should also be given here, again using maps to show boundaries between properties. Information on sub-divisions of properties, agricultural tenancies, grazing and other rights are all included in component 1.5 'Present Land-Use and Management'.

Physical Characteristics

Give a summary of the physical character of the site in terms of climate, geomorphology, geology and soils. These factors indirectly affect grazing because they strongly influence the vegetation of a site and hence also which animals are present. Detailed physical information is not likely to be necessary. More information will be required for factors which potentially interact with grazing management and this should be considered when writing this part of the plan. For example, if important geomorphological features are likely to be threatened by an expansion of woodland cover, such features need to be described. In a grazing plan, objectives will not be written for this sort of feature, but the relationship with grazing management should be discussed as a factor affecting the management of the key features (2.4). For some sites, it will be relevant to give a more detailed account of the soils, if habitat restoration or expansion is desirable, since soil information may help identify suitable areas for expansion.

Designations

All nature conservation or countryside designations for the site should be cited because these have implications for management, both in terms of options for funding and also in terms of restrictions on management activities. For example, in Britain, all non-marine SAC sites are SSSIs and some will be National Nature Reserves (NNRs). Maps should be included to indicate the boundaries of the designated areas. Also check for agricultural designations because these will influence the financial aid available to farmers. An example is the EU 'Less Favoured Areas' designation. Note any designations imposed by planning authorities. The implications for management of any designations should be discussed as factors affecting the management of the key features (2.4), with either a positive or negative influence on the options for management.

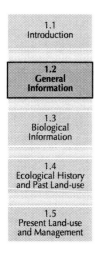

1.1
Introduction

1.2
General
Information

1.3
Biological
Information

1.4
Ecological History
and Past Land-use

1.5
Present Land-use
and Management

Historical and Archaeological Interest

Structures of archaeological interest or any historical value of the site should be mentioned. An example of the latter would be a site on which an important historical event occurred, resulting in the character of the site being of value. The amount of detail required here depends on the potential interaction with grazing management. For example, woodland development can be damaging to certain archaeological or historical features in which case the feature should be described here. The implications for grazing management should be fully discussed as factors affecting the management of the key features (2.4).

Landscape and Cultural Value

A site may have landscape value even if it does not have a national landscape designation. The site may be particularly valued in a local context for its landscape, or it may have other cultural interest to local people. This should be described briefly and any implications for management should be discussed as factors affecting the management of the key features (2.4).

Sources of Information

- **Other management plans for the site:** If plans have previously been prepared for your site, these will provide useful descriptive information. If the plan covers a site with a different boundary, this should be noted in the grazing plan and the information should be used selectively, because some information may be incomplete or inaccurate for your site. Existing plans may identify geological or archaeological features on the site and may also list other designations which apply, although it is worth checking that this information is up-to-date, unless the plan was recently prepared.

- **soils:** countrywide soil surveys; MLURI maps of soils in Scotland (see references).

- **boundaries of designated areas:** consult statutory nature conservation organisations and/or planning authorities

- **cultural interest:** consult local authorities and their local plans

- **land ownership:** local authorities will keep records; statutory conservation agencies should hold ownership information for designated sites

- **natural heritage and agricultural designations:** see Appendix 1 for information on these countryside designations in Scotland

- **archaeological interest:** consult national historical agencies

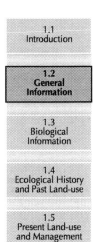

1.1
Introduction

1.2
General
Information

1.3
Biological
Information

1.4
Ecological History
and Past Land-use

1.5
Present Land-use
and Management

CASE STUDY: 1.2 General Information

This grazing management plan addresses part of the Torridon Forest Site of Special Scientific Interest (SSSI) (GR 890600) and the whole of the Beinn Eighe SSSI (GR 985625) which are two of the seven SSSIs within the Loch Maree Complex candidate Special Area of Conservation (cSAC). For the purposes of the grazing plan the name 'Torridon Hills site' will be applied to the part of the cSAC which includes these two SSSIs, and where more relevant the individual SSSI name will be referred to.

Torridon Hills site is located in the Ross and Cromarty region of NW Scotland and also lies within the Wester Ross National Scenic Area. The designations for the two sites are listed below. The site also lies within the agricultural designation of a Severely Disadvantaged Area and it is a crofting county.

Beinn Eighe:
National Nature Reserve
SSSI. Re-notified in 1985
UNESCO Biosphere Reserve
Council of Europe diploma-holding site
Nature Conservation Review site
Geological Review Site

Torridon Forest

SSSI. Renotified in 1986

Nature Conservation Review site
Geological Review Site

Map x shows the boundaries of the two SSSIs and the part of the cSAC which is included in this plan.

There are four owners within the cSAC boundary:
- The National Trust for Scotland owns most of Torridon Forest SSSI and part of the Beinn Eighe Reserve (506 ha). There is a National Nature Reserve Agreement with SNH, due for review in 1998.

- Grudie Estate owns ~ 900 ha of the Torridon Forest SSSI.

- Scottish Natural Heritage owns 4176 ha of Beinn Eighe NNR

- Kinlochewe Estate owns 1.7 ha of Beinn Eighe NNR.

Map x shows the ownership boundaries of the estates.

Torridon Hills is a rugged and mountainous region rising steeply to several ridges and tops reaching over 1000m. The area is rich in glaciated landforms including numerous lochs, hummocky moraines and deep corries. The sense of wilderness, remoteness and isolation of the landscape is of great value to visitors, climbers, walkers and mountaineers.

The vegetation communities and their floristics are strongly influenced by the climate and soils. The climate is hyperoceanic, with more than 220 annual wet days and precipitation exceeds evaporation for the whole year. The relatively mild and equable annual temperature range is countered by high exposure to prevailing winds. The geology is dominated by Cambrian quartzite overlying Torridonian sandstone. Soils are generally very base-poor, consisting largely of peats, peaty gleys, peaty podzols and rankers and alpine lithosols and regosols. There are considerable expanses of hummocky moraines with a thin peat cover and much exposed rock. At high altitudes, large areas of shattered quartzite rock produce immature soils, whilst extensive exposures of calcareous Serpulite Grit and base-rich Fucoid beds provide some local enrichment to soils, especially in particular areas on the Beinn Eighe SSSI.

The area has not been extensively surveyed for archaeological interests. There is evidence of human settlement from the early Bronze Age in the area around Torridon and shieling remains are indicated both on and outwith the cSAC.

1.3 Biological Information

- *description of flora*

- *description of fauna*

- *the contribution of grazing to the current pattern of vegetation*

Purpose

The biological information for a grazing plan is divided into three main sub-sections; 'Flora', 'Fauna' and 'The Contribution of Grazing to the Current Pattern of Vegetation'. Grazing will have a direct impact on the flora, and an indirect impact on the fauna, through its effect on the structure and composition of vegetation. The management of grazing is aimed at achieving objectives for key features, which may be plant species, plant communities and/or animal species. Grazing management will always be directed initially at the vegetation. For an animal species key feature, the aim of grazing management will be to maintain its habitat in terms of the structure and composition of vegetation.

The key features of the site are a sub-set of the total collection of biological features. Select the key features (described in 2.2) before writing the description of flora and fauna to ensure that the appropriate information is included here, and to avoid repetition between plan components. Information on the key features will be included in section 2.2 'Selection and Evaluation of the Key Features'.

Content

Points to consider when selecting information for the description of flora and fauna are:

- any feature for which there is survey information should be listed in the Description. Species can be grouped, instead of listed individually if not directly relevant to the management of grazing; for example if the site supports nationally rare invertebrates, it may be sufficient to indicate the number of species

- divide the information so that biological interest is summarised here in 1.3, but specific details of key features are provided in Part 2

1.3.1 Flora
Purpose

A full account of the vegetation at the site is essential for any grazing plan, including a basic description of the flora and information required in the decision-making process. The distribution and extent of vegetation types at the site determines the foraging patterns of large herbivores. This information is essential for predicting the incidence of grazing across the site, and in determining how to manipulate grazing patterns.

Content

This section should include an account of
- plant communities
- individual plant species of particular nature conservation value

1. Plant Communities

Describe the distribution and extent of plant communities. Aim to give a general account of the nature of the vegetation of the site, supplemented by maps produced in vegetation surveys. All of the major vegetation types should be described, including:
- those which cover large areas
- those of particular nature conservation value
- those which will influence decisions about grazing management because of their forage value; for example large areas of vegetation of little nutritional value, or areas of high forage quality

Where possible, use one vegetation classification system for the description to avoid confusion; a nationally recognised system is likely to be more appropriate than the CORINE (see Appendix 2) because the former will be more widely known. The system used is likely to be dictated by the vegetation survey information available, but if combining the results of more than one survey, convert between the systems used if possible. It may be desirable to convert survey information if this uses an old classification system which has been replaced by a new, widely used system. For example, in Britain, most upland sites will only have been fully surveyed by the Nature Conservancy Council's Upland Survey team in which vegetation was classified in the Birks and Ratcliffe system (see Appendix 2). This information can be used for the account of vegetation at a site, but it may be preferable to convert the information to the National Vegetation Classification (see Appendix 2).

In addition to the general description of vegetation, botanical key features also need to be considered here, but avoid repetition with component 2.2 of the plan, where specific details of the key features are given.

2. Plant Species of Nature Conservation Value

Individual plant species of note are those which have particular nature conservation value, in an international, national or local context. They should be mentioned in the description of flora. However, if such species are to be treated as key features, it is sufficient to note here the number of species within each rarity category, and to give details in component 2.2. Species of note which are not key features should be listed here and discussed as factors affecting the management of the key features (2.4).

Sources of Information

- Site Vegetation Surveys
  The most obvious sources of information on vegetation are survey reports. Note that survey information may have been digitised using a Geographical Information System which will make the production of maps easier; check with the country agency. Conversion between vegetation classification systems may not be ideal and should be treated with caution. This is discussed for the British situation in Appendix 2. Include details of

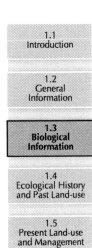

1.1
Introduction

1.2
General
Information

1.3
Biological
Information

1.4
Ecological History
and Past Land-use

1.5
Present Land-use
and Management

the surveys such as:
- what the survey covers, in terms of area and any specific vegetation types
- when the survey was done
- the method and vegetation classification system used; for example the uplands in Britain were covered by the NCC Upland Vegetation Survey in the 1980s, which was based on aerial photographs with sample ground truthing, and used the Birks and Ratcliffe system. These details are important for interpretation
- the accuracy and value of the survey; e.g. the NCC Upland Vegetation Survey of Britain is not accurate for communities that occur in small patches because of the method used.

- existing management plans where available

- citations of nature conservation designations for the site; for example in Britain, the SSSI citation should be consulted

- for information on the status of rare plant species in Scotland see bibliography

1.3.2 Fauna

Purpose

A description of fauna provides information on the biological interest of the site and details of wild herbivores.

Content

This section should include information on:
- wild herbivores (domestic species are discussed in 1.5 'Present Land-Use and Management')

- species of high nature conservation value

- species which are expected to be strongly influenced by any change in grazing management

- a list or description of other species can be included at the discretion of the planner but is not discussed here

The level of detail required varies as described below, but estimates of population size should be included where available, although in practice, information is likely to be available mainly for larger species such as deer, goats or ponies.

1. Wild Herbivores
Aim to give an account of all mammalian herbivores, or at least all large mammalian herbivores. This information may be needed later in the planning process to make management decisions or to try to determine the relative contribution of various herbivore species to the current grazing pressure at the site. Note that any management of wild species on the site is described in component 1.5, 'Present Land-Use and Management'. Estimates of population size may be made as part of the management of such species, so to avoid repetition, details of these species should be provided in 1.5 and cross-referenced here.

Where possible, the description of unmanaged herbivores should include:

■ estimates of population size; see 'Sources of Information'

■ a description of distribution, including seasonal, altitudinal and other spatial variations

Smaller species such as voles should at least be listed, but estimates of population size are unlikely to be available and in any case, it is difficult to predict their impact on vegetation. For the purposes of planning, unless these species are key features, they are not considered further.

Mention invertebrate herbivores, but note that their impact on vegetation is poorly understood, except for a few species, normally pest species. Provide details only of those known to be significant herbivores at the site. Population estimates are unlikely to be available or useful and it is more appropriate to describe the impact of these species.

2. Species of Particular Conservation Value

Animal species of particular nature conservation value will include those listed below, and they may or may not be treated as key features in the grazing plan:

■ birds cited in an SPA designation

■ Annex II species listed in the Habitats and Species Directive

■ Red Data species

■ in Britain, species which are scheduled in the Wildlife and Countryside Act, 1981

For most species, information on population size, distribution and breeding status should be included. Details of species threatened with disturbance or persecution, such as certain birds of prey, should be treated as confidential. Avoid repetition between the present description and the 'Selection and Evaluation of Key Features' in 2.2. Species of nature conservation value which are not key features should be discussed in 2.4 'Factors Influencing the Management of the Key Features'.

3. Species expected to be influenced by changes in grazing management

Certain changes in grazing regimes may strongly affect animal species, some of which may not have been covered in the two categories of fauna described so far and should therefore be mentioned separately. Examples are species of high nature conservation value that occur outside the area covered by the plan. For example, species on inbye land that is part of the same management unit as the hill land, or birds of prey that breed outside the designated area but are known to hunt there. List these species along with any information on their distribution or population size. The expected impact of changes to the grazing regime should be discussed in 2.4 'Factors Affecting the Management of the Key Features'.

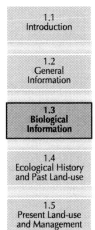

Sources of Information

- existing management plans, where available

- estimates of population size and distribution. The greatest amount of information is likely to be available for the larger species. Even if population size has not been estimated, land managers, farmers, stalkers and rangers will often have some observational information about the distribution and numbers of large herbivores. The information available will vary between sites

and there may often be very little or none. A lack of population information should be noted here and may need to be rectified for the purposes of managing some species. This is dealt with later in the planning process.

- for sites in Britain, SSSI citations will list some of the fauna

- for information on rare fauna in Scotland, see bibliography

1.3.3 The Contribution of Grazing to the Current Pattern of Vegetation

Purpose

This section aims to identify what is known about the impact of current and recent past grazing on the site and the role that this has played in the development of the range of vegetation types which now occur. Note that the present section specifically considers the impacts of current and recent grazing regimes, in contrast to component 1.4, which is a factual account of past management and long-term vegetation change.
This discussion will help to:

- identify whether the impact of grazing is currently positive or negative, and whether changes are required

- identify how much is known about spatial variations in the impact of grazing across the site

- identify vegetation types degraded by inappropriate grazing which might be restored as part of the grazing plan

Content

This description should summarise existing survey or anecdotal information on how grazing has influenced the development of the present vegetation. This should not be confused with detailed assessments of current condition of key features, or the current impact of grazing on the key features, which should be included in component 2.3 of the plan.

In this section include:
- accounts of any existing vegetation

types that indicate the impacts of grazing. For example, some types of grass-dominated sward have developed as a result of heavy grazing on heath vegetation, causing the woody species to be replaced by grasses. Recorded or anecdotal evidence may document the decline of the heath, or remnant plants of the woody species within the grass sward. Evidence of such an impact would suggest that grazing pressure is moderately heavy at the site, at least in places where this is occurring. Similarly if heath vegetation is being invaded by regeneration of scrub or trees, this would indicate a low grazing pressure. A discussion of such trends is sufficient here; an assessment of how the grazing pressure relates to the objectives is made later (2.5).

- any existing knowledge of spatial variations in grazing pressure on the site; there may be observational evidence or notes may have been made during vegetation surveys

Sources of Information

- vegetation surveys, particularly notes made by the surveyor

- site managers'/occupiers' knowledge of past vegetation

- anecdotal information about the site history

- documentary evidence of changes in vegetation and associated land management may help to determine the contribution of grazing in historical times

- detailed knowledge of the species composition of existing vegetation and an understanding of the ecological impacts of grazing

- aerial photographs; compare recent with older photographs where available for evidence of changes in the extent of vegetation types

1.1
Introduction

1.2
General
Information

1.3
Biological
Information

1.4
Ecological History
and Past Land-use

1.5
Present Land-use
and Management

1.4 Ecological History and Past Land-Use

- *past changes in vegetation*
- *past changes in herbivore populations*
- *past land-use of the site*

Purpose

This section is a factual account of past management practices, changes in herbivore numbers and major vegetation changes. The vegetation at the site will have been shaped over many years by a combination of soils, climate and management, including grazing. The purpose of this section is to help with the interpretation of vegetation patterns and to suggest what might be possible at the site.

Content

Past grazing management should be described in some detail, as should known changes in wild herbivore populations. It is also worth noting any other major land-use which may have contributed to the current pattern of vegetation; for example extensive burning. In addition, where available, details of vegetation history should be included to identify major changes over time, such as changes in woodland cover.

This section should aim to include details of the following, where possible:
- account of historical land-use and management practices
- trends in the presence of domestic herbivores over time, including indications of stocking densities and seasonal grazing patterns
- trends in populations of large wild herbivores, such as red deer and feral goats
- trends in populations of smaller herbivores if available
- trends in populations of introduced herbivore species; for example, rabbits in Britain
- changes in vegetation cover, including woodland cover and species composition
- changes in populations of rare plants for which records exist (if these species are key features, this information should be given in 2.3 instead)
- changes in populations of non-herbivores such as wolves

Sources of Information

This type of information can be extracted from a number of sources, some of which will not be site-specific, but patterns in vegetation change or land-use often occurred over large areas and general information may be of value. Ideally, site-specific information on animal numbers and vegetation should be collated but this may not always be available. Possible sources of information are as follows:

- historical records kept by the landowner, and in particular, records for large estates that document agricultural tenancies and accounts of sport shooting; these may also give descriptions of vegetation, particularly of woodland cover
- published descriptions of the history of the general area; try to verify the accuracy of these general accounts

for your site using the other sources mentioned because there may have been site-specific variations

- results of pollen analysis for the area, or for your site if available; these will indicate general trends such as changes in woodland cover

- local knowledge from current farmers/occupiers or from long-term inhabitants of the area

- archaeological records, which will indicate past occupance and possibly agricultural systems

CASE STUDY: 1.4 Ecological History and Past Land-Use

1.4.1 Woodland Cover and Decline
Information about the prehistoric extent of woodland and its decline at this site has been derived from a study of peat columns collected on the site of a Neolithic axe quarry on Ben Lawers (Tipping *et al.*, 1993). There is evidence in the pollen record of *Corylus*, *Sorbus*, *Betula* and probably *Ulmus*, which were thought to have formed dense woodland. Tall herb communities were present and at this time may have been associated with woodland. Early decline of woodland in approximately 5950 BC and 4000 BC is thought to have been caused mainly by climate changes, but there is evidence to suggest that further decline may have been associated with human activity. Grazing animals became increasingly important to Neolithic people and woodland was cleared to provide pasture.

1.4.2 Agricultural History
Information about agriculture in historic times has been extracted from Bil (1996), which discusses the land-use history of the areas in and around the Ben Lawers SSSI and The National Trust for Scotland property, between the 16th and 19th centuries. The hill land on Ben Lawers was used for summer grazing of livestock and peat cutting. Farms situated near Loch Tay kept sheep, cattle and horses. Cultivation of the land during the historical period is thought to have been practised only on a strip of land approximately half a mile wide, between the loch and the lower slopes of the hill, according to the infield-outfield agricultural system. A head dyke separated good arable land from the higher altitude hill grazings and muir and this facilitated the management of domestic stock. The southern boundary of The National Trust for Scotland property is approximately coterminous with the old dyke.

For the purposes of this plan, historical hill grazing patterns are of primary interest. Stock were grazed on the hill in summer during the 16th and 17th centuries when the shieling tradition was practised. Hill grazings were communal, shared between many communities. The number of stock grazed by each farm and the timing of grazing were tightly restricted by the estate owner to avoid over-use and ensure even distribution of this resource between communities, in the absence of march boundaries. However, Bil (1996) provides no details of the densities of animals on the hill, or how limits were set. A type of blackfaced sheep was introduced in the 17th century and sheep numbers increased sharply in the 18th century, replacing cattle. The shieling tradition declined during the late 18th century as estates turned over hill land for sheep farms and the Scottish blackface sheep was developed and introduced on a large scale. As a result, grazing pressure on hill land became intense. Sheep farming is still the main landuse on much of the cSAC today. Information on recent sheep numbers is based purely on grazing rights and management agreements and is given in 1.5

1.4.3 Peat Cutting
Peat was essential to the people along Loch Tay during the 17th - 19th centuries, when it was used as house-building material, a fertiliser and as fuel for burning lime for construction. Peat cutting was extensive on Ben Lawers and evidence can be seen on the hill near Meall Odhar at an altitude of 530-610 m and on Ben Lawers and Ben Ghlas at 680-760 m. In some places, bogs were exhausted by the removal of peat, but even where cutting was less significant, it could have a considerable impact on the landscape. Erosion channels in bogs today for example, may have been initiated by repeated peat cutting.

1.5 Present Land-Use and Management

- *current land-use*
- *the current pattern of tenure and occupation*
- *management of wild and/or domestic herbivores*

This section documents the current land-use of the site. This includes details of management units (1.5.1), agricultural tenancies, the objectives of site owners and occupiers, and site management practices. Emphasise the current management of wild and/or domestic herbivores and vegetation management.

1.5.1 Management Units
Purpose

The aim of this section is to describe the current pattern of occupation on the site and to indicate the scale at which site management varies. Ownership boundaries (tenure) were provided under 'General Information' (1.2). Give full details of all management units (see Information box 1) in the present section. Any rights or agreements affecting the management of the land should be described because these may influence the options for implementing a new grazing regime. The implications of such agreements are discussed as factors affecting the management of the key features (2.4).

INFORMATION BOX 1: Management Units

Management units indicate the scale at which management of the land varies or is controlled. An area designated for conservation may include several properties with different owners. These properties may be the management units, unless they are sub-divided into units with different occupiers or management systems; for example agricultural tenancies; in which case these will be the management units.

Content

This section should include details of:

- occupiers/agricultural holdings or tenancies; including sufficient information to determine the options for changes to these arrangements, such as the length of the lease, and whether it is transferable if the leaseholder gives up

- grazing rights; including details of the legal standing of such rights and options for change to stocking rates

- shooting rights held by anyone other than the owner of a property

- other agreements, such as rights for supplementary feeding on the site

- physical boundaries between units which constrain the movements of large herbivores; including natural and artificial boundaries. For the latter, indicate why and when these were erected and whether they are still effective

- Maps showing all of the above information

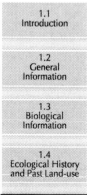

1.1
Introduction

1.2
General
Information

1.3
Biological
Information

1.4
Ecological History
and Past Land-use

1.5
Present Land-use
and Management

Sources of Information

- Owners and occupiers should be approached for information on tenancies and other agreements. This will be the main source of information.

- For sites in Britain, there may be information on management units in SSSI notification documents. Unless the site was notified recently, the accuracy of this information should be checked by enquiring with the owners listed.

- There may be existing management agreements between owners or occupiers and the statutory nature conservation body; for example in Britain, SSSI management agreements. Check with the statutory agency.

- Existing management plans should provide a source of information on ownership and tenancies. A description of tenure and grazing rights in Scotland is given in Appendix 3.

1.5.2 Present Land-Use
Purpose

This section describes the main land-uses and management activities of owners or occupiers of each management unit. These may conflict with the nature conservation aims for the site, and the implications are discussed as factors affecting the management of the key features (2.4). Details of land management, along with observations of the vegetation, can be used later to estimate what changes of management are required. For example, if the number of sheep on a site is known and the vegetation is undergrazed, recommendations for sheep numbers can be based on this existing knowledge.

Content

Present land-use information should be included for each management unit because management may vary between tenancies or other units, even where these are part of the same property. Provide details of the major land-use systems, with particular attention to herbivores; including domestic stock and populations of wild herbivores which are managed in any way. For each unit, describe the following:

- all land-uses/objectives of owners or occupiers

- nature conservation management

- domestic stock management practices

- management of wild herbivores

- specific details of the other management practices which are likely to have a strong impact on the vegetation should be given; for example, burning

For the purposes of these plans, information about the management of herbivores and management for nature conservation is essential and is described further here.

Domestic stock management
Where possible, the following details should be included for each management unit for the stock grazed on the site:

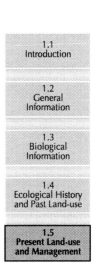

1.1
Introduction

1.2
General
Information

1.3
Biological
Information

1.4
Ecological History
and Past Land-use

1.5
**Present Land-use
and Management**

- type of animal, e.g. sheep, cattle

- breed and sex of stock

- numbers of animals grazed on each management unit which is wholly or partly within the cSAC; densities can be calculated but these may not be accurate unless the units are separated by physical boundaries restricting animal movements

- seasonal variations in numbers of animals

- distribution of stock. This information will help the planner to predict where grazing pressure is likely to be high and low. Animals will not be evenly distributed, and as a result, the impact of grazing on vegetation will also vary. Note physical boundaries within or around the site that restrict stock. If there are no restrictions on stock movement, do not assume that the distribution of domestic stock will be the same as the distribution of grazing rights or tenancies.

- stock management practices such as tupping, lambing, replacements (Appendix 4)

- lambing percentages

- supplementary feeding; where and when

Wild Herbivore Management
Details of the populations of wild herbivores should be included where these are available. Describe herbivores which are managed in some way by landowners or occupiers, but information on other wild herbivores should have been included as part of the description of 'Fauna'(1.3.2).
Include here:

- estimates of population size and sex ratios, including a description and evaluation of the methods used to estimate these parameters

- details of distribution across the site and seasonal ranging patterns

- details of how these animals are managed, the location of feeding sites, cull figures, how culls are set, numbers shot for sport

Sources of Information

Many of the details of current management practices will be available only from the owner, manager or occupier of the land and acquisition of this information depends on their willingness to provide it. Below, information sources are suggested and the use of each is discussed, but bear in mind the accuracy of each.

- **Land owners/occupiers/graziers** are the main source of information, so speak to them first.

- **Tenancy agreements** or legal grazing rights will define the number of animals permitted on a given area of land, and may even specify seasonal patterns. These sources are useful indicators of

numbers, but not accurate because the grazier may be over- or under-stocking. If this is the main source of information on stocking rates, it should be made clear that these are assumed numbers of stock. Even if it is possible to question farmers about stocking rates, this information may not be accurate since they are unlikely to admit if they are exceeding a legal limit. Grazing rights for sheep may specify only the number of adult sheep permitted, but there may also be lambs present.

- **Observational counts** of domestic stock may have been done, for example on nature reserves, or domestic stock may have been counted during deer counts. This information would give an indication of stocking rates, but accuracy is limited by visibility and weather, as well as fluctuations in the number of animals put on the hill. For example, sheep are gathered for clipping and to remove lambs, and counts may coincide with days when numbers are unusually low. (Appendix 4)

■ **Counts** of wild animals are often made as part of their management. For example, red deer population size is estimated by many private estates in Scotland; usually by observation; and the Deer Commission for Scotland perform their own counts. This information can be acquired from the Deer Commission, however, returns from the deer management groups can only be provided with the permission of the group. Details of these and other counting methods are given in Appendix 5. Care should be taken in the interpretation of count information, because accuracy varies with method.

■ Agricultural advisory services

■ Information on the **distribution of animals** across the site may be available from the farmer or land manager. For example, if sheep are shepherded, the shepherd should know where the animals spend most of their time. Similarly, a site manager should have information on the distribution of managed wild herbivores. Where red deer are culled or shot for sport, the stalker will have a good knowledge of seasonal ranging patterns. In both wild and domestic herbivores, distribution can vary with season.

In the absence of good records of animal distribution, it may be possible to make predictions. The distribution of herbivores depends on a number of factors, including the availability of food, shelter and weather patterns. The relative importance of each factor

varies between herbivore species. Details of the factors which influence the distribution of large herbivores are given in Appendices 6, 7, 8. If supplementary feed is provided for either domestic or wild herbivores, this will strongly influence their distribution, and also the grazing pressure on vegetation surrounding feeding sites.

■ Always note inaccuracies in your information, or assumptions made. Typical assumptions are: actual stocking rates are equivalent to the number of grazing rights and lambs are often not included in density calculations because their grazing activity is assumed to be very low (if lambs are included, explain how many sheep equivalents were used to estimate grazing by lambs). If distribution information is lacking, explain what information was used to make predictions about distribution, or whether the animals were assumed to be fairly evenly distributed.

The above list defines the ideal information which should be collated. In many cases, this level of detail will not be available. If there is no other information on the numbers of stock grazed on the site, or on the populations of wild herbivores, it may be necessary to count them in order to make decisions. At this stage, it is necessary to include only the information which is available. If new information is required this will be evident in Part 2 of the plan, where gaps in information will be identified as projects.

Nature Conservation
Describe any current site management which is aimed at meeting nature conservation objectives, such as heather burning or exclosures erected to protect vegetation from grazing. Sources of information are:
■ site managers or owners

■ management plans or management agreements

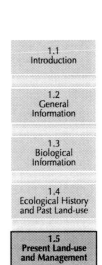

1.1
Introduction

1.2
General
Information

1.3
Biological
Information

1.4
Ecological History
and Past Land-use

1.5
**Present Land-use
and Management**

- site records held by country agencies

Other Management Practices

Other land-uses can influence grazing management; details of these should be given for the site. For each, aim to define the management practices and the expected implications for grazing management. Some of the major land-uses in the uplands are discussed below.

- **Forestry.** Describe woodland blocks or plantations adjacent to the site if the herbivores have access to these blocks. Large herbivores will use woodlands for shelter and in bad weather the animals will be attracted to these areas, which can result in heavy grazing pressure adjacent to woodlands (see Appendices 6, 7 and 8 for information on the factors which influence the distribution of large herbivores).

- **Recreation.** Upland sites are frequently subject to heavy recreational pressure, including hill walking and skiing. Describe visitor numbers, seasonal patterns in numbers, spatial variations in visitor pressure and any known impacts of recreation at the site, such as trampling damage to vegetation. Heavy visitor pressure can indirectly influence grazing management. For example, large numbers of visitors can disturb wild herbivores and affect their distribution. Red and sika deer may respond to this disturbance by using the site mostly at night, with important implications for their management. For sites managed for recreation, detailed information on visitor use may be recorded although for privately owned sites this may not be relevant. Try to gather local knowledge. Any known impacts of recreation on grazing animals or grazing management should be discussed as factors affecting the management of the key features (2.4).

- **Sport shooting** of species other than large herbivores, such as grouse. The associated land management, such as heather burning, should be described, following discussions with landowners/gamekeepers.

CASE STUDY: 1.5 Present Land-Use and Management

1.5.1 Management Units

The two estates E and F are in hand and these parts of the estates within the cSAC constitute management units. The National Trust for Scotland (NTS) property is sub-divided into five management units managed by three tenants. Various arrangements give the NTS different degrees of control over the land and its management but only four of the five units now have sheep run on them. The five units shown on Map x are:

Units I and II: Area 560 ha and 729 ha respectively. These are full agricultural tenancies which are heritable and are expected to be handed to the present tenant's son in the near future. Currently, father and son work the units together. The number of sheep agreed in the tenancy are 550 breeding ewes on each unit.

Unit III: This is a limited partnership lease, renewable at 5 yearly intervals. The tenant is Mr. B. who runs its 349 ha with his neighbouring 1250 ha estate which adjoins this management unit. The number of sheep agreed are 100 breeding ewes.

Units IV and V: The areas are about 480 ha and 520 ha respectively. The tenant is a retired ranger for the NTS and lives in the steading A. Along with a relative, they also shepherd for Mr. B (estate F). There is an informal 'gentleman's' agreement between the tenant and the NTS for the grazing of 120 sheep. This agreement is reviewed annually.

The NTS management units are arranged so that each has some fenced inbye on the valley 'flats' with a greater proportion of the unit being rough grazing on the hill. The inbye consists of relatively small areas of varying quality grassland, some having been improved in the past. No crops are taken off this ground. Unit I is enclosed by fencing around its lower slopes. All the remaining management units are unfenced and the boundaries follow topographical features such as ridge tops or valleys. Although the topography is extremely precipitous in places, there is ultimately no barrier to sheep movement between these units and also neighbouring estates.

Estate E: About 400ha of the south facing steep slopes of H. Glen lies within the south-eastern section of cSAC but it is part of a much larger estate extending to the south and east of the cSAC.

Estate F: about 300 ha of the south-west facing slopes of Gleann F. lies within the cSAC. This is part of 1250 ha estate which extends further south and west.

1.5.2 Present Land-Use

The primary objectives of the NTS are promotion of nature conservation, education and responsible public recreational use of the mountain areas. Agricultural use which is consistent with these objectives is also encouraged and the long-term vision is for the main pastoral area to be confined to the lower valleys. Estate F is predominantly a sheep farming enterprise and the prime objective for Estate E is management for commercial deer stalking.

The dominant agricultural land-use currently is grazing by Scottish Blackface sheep. Shepherding is usually carried out jointly by the tenants and the sheep are managed in a similar hillfarm system on all units. Ewes are tupped either on the hill or on inbye land during November and they are turned out onto the hill where most lambing occurs from late April for about one month. Lambing percentages range from 75%-90%. Gathering of the flocks is done in July for shearing and dipping of ewes, counting and marking male lambs, and in autumn for these and draft ewes to go to market. At this time, strayed animals are also sorted. About 25%-30% of the ewe-hoggs are kept for flock replacements and on all but one unit, they are wintered away from early October to April 1st. The numbers of sheep given below are estimates for each management unit, collated by Trust staff in 1996.

Units I and II: Summer stocking on unit I is 500 ewes plus lambs (est.400) and 120 returned ewe-hoggs. Winter stocking is about 530 breeding ewes and 15 rams. There is some supplementary winter feeding on the lower parks. Also kept on the lower ground

1.1
Introduction

1.2
General
Information

1.3
Biological
Information

1.4
Ecological History
and Past Land-use

1.5
Present Land-use
and Management

of this unit are about 42 Highland cattle - sixteen cows, two heifers, ten 1 yr old bulls and calves with the numbers controlled by the extent of suitable winter grazing. Limited winter feeding with hay takes place on the in-bye at the foot of the hill or on the parks across the trunk road. Summer stocking of Unit II is 520 breeding ewes, lambs (est. 400) and 150 ewe-hoggs and supplementary feeding occurs on the semi-improved inbye in the valley flats.

Unit III: This unit is run with the adjoining estate F. Winter stocking is 120 breeding ewes and 6 rams. Summer stocking is 110 ewes plus lambs and 36 ewe-hoggs returned from wintering away. The two boggy fenced in-bye fields which were once drained and fertilised are used for supplementary winter feeding with feed blocks.

Units IV and V: Sheep were gradually removed from unit V until none were present by early 1996. There are currently no commercial stock grazing on this unit except for occasional sheep straying from unit IV. Summer flock on unit IV is about 230 breeding ewes plus about 150 lambs and the surviving ewe-hoggs. Winter stocking is estimated at 236 breeding ewes plus 8 rams and 58 ewe-hoggs wintered on the unit. Stock are on the hill over-winter with no supplementary winter feeding.

Estate F: There are about 1150 ewes grazed on the entire 1250 ha. Assuming an average stocking density of 1.0 ewe ha^{-1}, about 300 ewes may be grazing this part of the cSAC, but the distribution of the ewes depends on forage quality and weather conditions. The sheep may be hefted to this area but this is not known for certain and since there is an access gate to the tenanted unit III there may be some movement into the other units. Supplementary winter feeding with hay and blocks takes place on the inbye land of unit III and on the estate hill (off the cSAC area) where accessible by vehicle.

Deer Management

Estate E: This is managed as a traditional sporting estate in conjunction with adjoining estates under the same ownership. The only figures for deer numbers on estate E comes from the 1995 Red Deer Commission (RDC) count: 48 stags, 32 hinds and 14 calves. On the adjoining estates the count total in the same year was 1430.

The **National Trust for Scotland:** The policy is aimed at maintaining a stable low population and a healthy sex ratio and an annual cull is carried out if required. The 1995 RDC count: 130 deer total, 102 stags, 14 hinds and 8 calves.

Estate F: There are no RDC counts since red deer are rarely seen on this estate and there is neither culling nor sport shooting.

Distribution of sheep and red deer

There are no systematic counts of sheep numbers or records of distribution on the cSAC and it is assumed that in summer most of the estimated 1100 ewes and lambs from units II, III and IV range widely to find preferred forage. Stock on unit II is contained by fencing. The vegetation types of the montane area are strongly influenced by the complex topography, and very variable edaphic and climatic factors. Evidence from sheep dung and observed animals indicates that sheep move up the valleys, over the main ridges and into high altitude corries to locate preferred forage (predominantly grasslands and grassy dwarf shrub habitats in summer). Estate F is more topographically distinct, dominated by mat-grass but with areas of better quality grasses in the glen floor. Sheep may be hefted to this area, but since it is run with unit III, some may also move onto the hill and into other management units.

The number and distribution of red deer is known mainly from RDC counts and anecdotal information, the best being for NTS property which includes two mountains east of the cSAC. The numbers were counted weekly between Jan-Aug 1996 and the location of groups of hinds, stags and calves were mapped (see Map z). Numbers ranged between 90-200. Within the cSAC, the most used areas in these months were the slopes of the four main valleys, the south-east ridge and slopes of estate E. By far the highest numbers and heaviest use was recorded in valley G (adjoining but outside the cSAC) where sheep have been absent since 1994 and which is adjacent to other sporting estates. The few deer recorded in the most western areas may reflect the comparatively high usage by walkers and sheep but night occupancy might be higher. Detailed counts and

1.1
Introduction

1.2
General
Information

1.3
Biological
Information

1.4
Ecological History
and Past Land-use

1.5
Present Land-use
and Management

30   *Part 1*

Part 2
OBJECTIVES AND MANAGEMENT

This part of a grazing plan is the 'working document'; it is this part which will be most frequently used because it discusses the recommendations for grazing management and an analysis of some other options. Part 2 of the plan should be viewed as an active document because the planning process is not static. This part of the document is the most likely to change in subsequent reviews of the plan, whilst the Description will often be copied into later documents. Recommendations made in the plan are based on currently available information, but over time, new information should be fed back into the process to improve proposals for grazing management. This part of the plan defines the following:

- what is required for the site; the objectives

- what needs to be done to achieve the objectives in terms of a grazing management strategy

- how this strategy can be implemented

This part of the manual leads the user through the decision-making stages of planning in which the information collated as described in Part 1 is interpreted and used to make those decisions. In these stages, it may become evident that there are gaps in information that need to be filled before decisions about grazing management can be made with any degree of confidence. This is not to say that new information must be gathered before the plan can be completed, but the plan must note the need to gather the information. New information can then be used to feed into the decision-making process for later drafts of the grazing plan, improving upon earlier predictions and recommendations. Throughout Part 2, any need to collect new information or data should be defined as a project, displayed in a numbered project box. In the example below, showing Information Project 2.3.1, this is the first project listed in component 2.3 (Objectives, Current Condition and Impacts of Grazing). These Information Projects should then be listed in 2.7 'Prescriptions' as part of the work programme, along with herbivore management and monitoring projects.

EXAMPLE BOX 3: Information Project 2.3.1
Define targets and limits of change for willow scrub using the report (reference) to be produced in early 1998.

The Thought Process Leading to Recommendations for Grazing Management

DEVELOPING GRAZING MANAGEMENT RECOMMENDATIONS

Define the ideal grazing pattern for each key feature (2.3.4).

⬇

Compare the ideal patterns for the range of key features, to select an ideal grazing pattern for the whole site (2.5.1).

⬇

Discuss the practical herbivore management needed to achieve the grazing regime (2.5.2).

⬇

Make recommendations for practical herbivore management (2.5.3).

Recommendations for grazing management are developed in several stages. Firstly, the key features have to be selected because these define the reasons for management. Objectives for these key features are written next, which specify what is required. Grazing management is aimed at achieving these objectives. There are various steps in the process of making decisions about grazing management, shown in the box 'Developing Grazing Management Recommendations' along with the number of the relevant section in the manual.

INFORMATION BOX 2: Grazing Pattern

For this planning process, it is crucial to understand the difference between a grazing pattern and herbivore management/stocking regime or grazing regime. In this manual, a grazing pattern describes **where**, **when** and **how much grazing** is required. It does not include any specification of a number, density or type of herbivores.

Grazing animals should be viewed as tools used to achieve a desired grazing pattern. Animal management is constrained by a number of practical problems that will determine whether an ideal grazing pattern can be implemented. Considering the animal management necessary to achieve this grazing pattern is the final step in the planning process.

As an example, consider a situation in which the ideal grazing pattern would be to only have grazing in winter. This specifies what grazing is required, but is not a recommendation for animal management; the practicalities of achieving that pattern are considered in the next step of the process. The planner has to consider the options for managing those animals in order to have winter-only grazing. It may not be feasible and the planner will have to consider other options, but the purpose of an ideal grazing pattern is that the ideal has been noted for future reference.

Throughout this text, the term 'grazing pattern' will always mean the intensity/distribution/timing of grazing rather than the number/species/type of animal.

'Grazing regime' is also used, but with a more general meaning, incorporating any aspect of grazing management such as herbivore numbers or grazing pressure.

2.1 Obligations and Policies

- define why the site is being managed

- provide a framework for selecting key features

- identify any constraints on management imposed by land-use designations or policies

Prior to setting objectives, it is necessary to assess any obligations associated with designations or policies that apply to the site. This part of the grazing plan aims to define an overall Policy for the management plan and also to note any external policies or obligations that may restrict the options for practical management. For the purposes of these grazing plans, designations, obligations and policies can be allocated to two main categories, which influence the management of the site in different ways:

■ nature conservation designations

■ policies or designations that affect land-use

These categories are discussed below and a process is described for selecting the information to include in this component of a grazing plan.

2.1.1 Nature Conservation Designations

In the context of these grazing plans, nature conservation designations define the main reasons for managing the site, provide a framework for the selection of objectives in 2.2 and can be used to prioritise key features if necessary, in 2.5. A site may have more than one nature conservation designation but it may not be desirable to comply with all of them in the grazing plan. There are two types of designation to consider here: statutory and non-statutory; there is a legal obligation to comply with statutory designations. Rank the list of designations for the site and, in consultation with the country agency, select the designations the plan will comply with.

There is a basic hierarchy of designations to follow:
■ European obligations under the Habitats and Species Directive and the Birds Directive for SAC and SPA designated sites respectively (Natura 2000 sites). See Appendix 9 for the requirements specified in the Habitats and Species Directive.

■ National statutory designations for the site or nationally protected features. For example in Britain, the site may be an SSSI and individual species present may be listed in the schedules of the Wildlife and Countryside Act, 1981, which affords them legal protection.

■ Non-statutory local nature conservation designations or interests.

In some circumstances, the ranking of designations could vary from this standard, if for example a Natura 2000 site supports a feature of exceptional national value not cited in the European designation. Any change of priority would need to made in consultation with the country agency.

In the plan, present a list of the designations to be considered, rank these selected designations and record any differences in priority between features cited in the same designation. For example, SAC qualifying habitats have a higher rank than occurring features, and 'priority' (see Appendix 9) features have a higher rank than others.

DEALING WITH NATURE CONSERVATION DESIGNATIONS

Consult with statutory agencies to find all nature conservation designations for the site

⬇

Rank the designations

⬇

Determine which designations the plan will comply with

⬇

List these designations

⬇

Rank the designations in order of priority

⬇

Summarise with a statement of the main reasons for managing the site

---

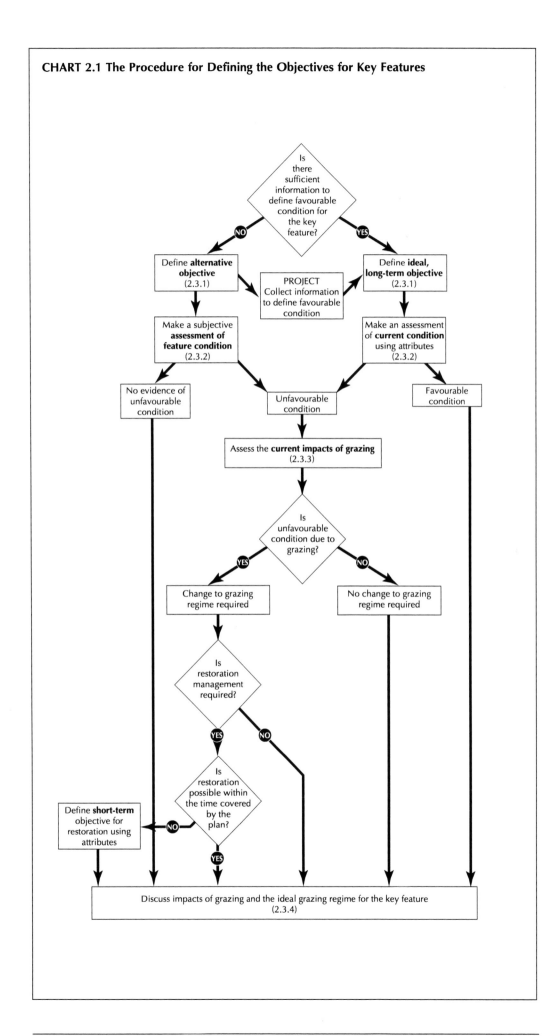

CHART 2.1 The Procedure for Defining the Objectives for Key Features

Is there sufficient information to define favourable condition for the key feature?

NO → Define **alternative objective** (2.3.1)

YES → Define **ideal, long-term objective** (2.3.1)

PROJECT Collect information to define favourable condition

Make a subjective **assessment of feature condition** (2.3.2)

Make an assessment of **current condition** using attributes (2.3.2)

No evidence of unfavourable condition

Unfavourable condition

Favourable condition

Assess the **current impacts of grazing** (2.3.3)

Is unfavourable condition due to grazing?

YES → Change to grazing regime required

NO → No change to grazing regime required

Is restoration management required?

YES / NO

Is restoration possible within the time covered by the plan?

NO → Define **short-term** objective for restoration using attributes

YES

Discuss impacts of grazing and the ideal grazing regime for the key feature (2.3.4)

2.1 Obligations and policies

2.2 Selection & evaluation of the key features

2.3 Objectives, current condition and impacts of grazing on the key features

2.4 Factors affecting the management of the key features

2.5 Rationale and recommendations for grazing management

2.6 Monitoring projects

2.7 Prescriptions

2.1.2 Policies or Designations Affecting Land-Use

The options for managing a site can be constrained by a range of obligations associated with land-use policies or designations. Some of these may be statutory designations which carry legal obligations, but non-statutory requirement should also be considered in the planning process where possible. In the plan, list the range of obligations and indicate any requirements to comply with statutory obligations. The implications of any designations or policies for land management should be discussed in 2.4 'Factors Influencing the Management of the Key Features'.

Policies and designations which could influence the options for management include:

- statutory designations

- landscape designations

- statutory land-use policies, as may be defined by planning authorities

- policies/obligations of site owners; for example, the site may be owned by an organisation with a responsibility to consider landscape or access

- landscape, historical designations

2.1
Obligations and policies

2.2
Selection & evaluation of the key features

2.3
Objectives, current condition and impacts of grazing on the key features

2.4
Factors affecting the management of the key features

2.5
Rationale and recommendations for grazing management

2.6
Monitoring projects

2.7
Prescriptions

CASE STUDY: 2.1 Obligations & Policies

2.1.1 Statutory nature conservation obligations

This grazing plan is aimed at meeting nature conservation objectives for Ben Lawers cSAC. The site must be managed in compliance with the following:

- Directive 92/43/EEC on the Conservation of Natural Habitats and of Wild Flora and Fauna (Habitats Directive); site selected as cSAC for Annex I habitats

- Wildlife and Countryside Act, 1981; protection of scheduled species and the features cited in the SSSI designations.

The Habitats Directive requires that the Annex I habitats are maintained or restored at favourable conservation status. At the site level, this is defined for each habitat as favourable condition.

Article 6 of the Habitats Directive describes the 'Site Protection Obligations' and states the following responsibilities for SACs:

Article 6.2 requires that appropriate steps are taken 'to avoid.......the deterioration of natural habitats and the habitats of species...'; in this case, the Annex I habitats.

Article 6.3 requires that any plan or project not directly connected with or necessary to the management of the site but which is likely to have a significant effect on the site must undergo an appropriate assessment. The assessment required will depend on the project and would be guided by SNH.

Ben Lawers supports two priority habitats and as such, any project which could damage the site may only be considered in cases relating to human health or public safety, to beneficial consequences of primary importance for the environment or, subject to agreement from the European Commission other reasons of overriding public interest.

The features cited as reasons for the statutory designations are ranked as follows, beginning with the highest priority features:

- qualifying 'priority' habitats listed in Annex I of the Habitats Directive

- other qualifying Annex I habitats

- occurring/hosted 'priority' habitats

- other occurring/hosted Annex I habitats

- features cited in the SSSI designation and Schedule 8 species listed in the Wildlife and Countryside Act, 1981

2.1.2 NTS Policy

The part of the cSAC in The National Trust for Scotland (NTS) ownership is subject to the policies and objectives of the organisation. The statutory aims of NTS are set down in its enabling legislation, The National Trust for Scotland Order Confirmation Acts of 1935 and 1938 which state the purpose of NTS; essentially to protect its properties permanently for the benefit of the nation and to provide access to its properties for the public. General principles for the conservation and management of land are:

- NTS will give the highest priority to nature and landscape conservation interests, managing in a long term and sustainable manner.

- NTS will give a high priority to maintaining the economic viability, distinctive way of life and cultural traditions, without prejudice to its policies on nature and landscape conservation

- On mountain properties, NTS will respect the special qualities of these areas, following the spirit of the principles expressed by Percy Unna; the 'Unna Principles'.

The 'Unna Principles', specify that the land should be maintained in its 'primitive' condition with unrestricted access to the public; where primitive means not less primitive than at the time of purchase. Full details are given in the Ben Lawers NNR management plan (in prep.).

2.1
Obligations
and policies

2.2
Selection & evaluation
of the key features

2.3
Objectives, current
condition and impacts
of grazing on the
key features

2.4
Factors affecting the
management of the
key features

2.5
Rationale and
recommendations for
grazing management

2.6
Monitoring projects

2.7
Prescriptions

(Case Study: 2.1 Obligations & Policies - continued)
NTS specific aims for the Ben Lawers property are: to conserve the flora, to ensure conservation of other important wildlife and its landscape and cultural remains, to ensure open access while minimising adverse effects on the interests of the site, to provide interpretation and education and to manage the property in a manner which is beneficial to the local community.

2.1.3 Other Designations
There are statutory obligations associated with the Loch Rannoch and Glen Lyon National Scenic Area (NSA). This designation is aimed at controlling development and the planning authorities are required to seek advice from SNH about possible developments within the NSA. The site is within the Breadalbane ESA, but this scheme is voluntary and carries no legal requirements.

2.2 Selection and Evaluation of the Key Features

- select the key features

- describe how the key features are represented at the site

- evaluate and rank the key features, in terms of their status

This section of the manual describes the selection of key features; those features regarded as being the most important features at the site in the context of the plan, and at which grazing management is aimed. These features drive the decisions made about the grazing regime for the site.

The selection of key features in this manual is based on designations; key features are selected from these classifications and as such have already been evaluated, but some evaluation information is included in the grazing plan.

2.2.1 Selecting the Key Features

Key features are those features for which an objective will be written. For the purposes of these grazing plans, they are a sub-set of the range of biological features at the site, selected on the basis of nature conservation value. Key features will be cited as reasons for site designations or included in lists of rare or threatened species.

A process for selecting the key features is shown in the box. Note that two options are shown for the list of key features. One of these options should be selected, but note that features of high nature conservation value should always be treated as key features, even if they are not expected to be affected by grazing. For sites which are both SPA and SAC, there may be bird species which are unlikely to be affected by changes in grazing, but these should be included as key features to note that they have an equal status to SAC features. This will also ensure that these features are considered in the decision-making process, which is important because even if grazing does not affect them, management required to manipulate grazing might. For example, bird species susceptible to fence strike would be affected by the erection of fences.

A PROCESS FOR SELECTING KEY FEATURES

Compile a list of the features cited as reasons for the site designations. Also include other features of value with no designations, e.g. nationally rare species; this is the total list of possible features.

⬇

Consider the designations to be covered by the plan and the ranking of these from 2.1. Select the features cited for these designations, plus other features of value and rank these.

⬇

Consider that an objective needs to be written for all of the features; select the features for which this is desirable. Ensure there is no overlap between features cited in different designations e.g. species cited in one designation may be components of habitats cited in another; include only the habitat as a key feature.

⬇

Option 1:
List the remaining features; these are the key features

⬇

Consider the importance of grazing; is grazing expected to affect all of the features so far listed? Remove features which grazing is not expected to affect.

⬇

Option 2:
List the remaining features; these are the key features

2.2.2 Evaluation of Key Features

Along with a list of the key features, some evaluation information should be presented in the plan. The key features were selected from existing designations or lists of rare species. This means that the conservation value of the key features has been assessed in either an international, national or local context. For this reason, it is not considered necessary to fully evaluate the features as described by Ratcliffe (1977) or CCW (1996).

Natura 2000 features have been evaluated in a European context. Firstly, the inclusion of habitats and species in the Birds Directive or the Habitats and Species Directive indicates the value of these features in the European context. Furthermore, in the selection of SAC sites at the national level, the European interests represented at each site have been evaluated in the process of identifying 'qualifying' features (see Appendix 9).

2.2.3 Describing the Key Features in the Plan

Detailed information of the key features, where available, should be included in the plan. This supplements the information on the biological interests of the site provided in 1.3. Specific details are included in Part 2 of the plan because this information is of value when writing objectives. It is also more logical to describe the key features after they have been identified in the plan.

To compile this section, first list the key features with an indication of their status and, for plant communities, vegetation classification information. Additionally, describe how the key features occur at the site, if known.

Listing the Key Features
Basic information on the key features can be included in tabular form, similar to the specimen shown in Example box 4. Where appropriate create separate tables for plant species, animal species and habitats. Include the following information:
- a list of the key features, using the name/classification system that corresponds with the designation on which they are cited; so, for example, SAC qualifying Annex I habitats should be listed using the CORINE code and name.

- show the conservation status of each feature; such as SAC Annex I habitat (indicate 'qualifying', 'occurring' or 'priority' where appropriate), species listed on SPA proposal, red data species.

- for Annex I habitats, show the plant communities which represent the CORINE categories at the site, using the recognised national system; e.g. for sites in Britain, see Appendix 2. Check with survey information to find out which communities occur at the site.

- for plant communities, show the conversion between the classification system used in designation citations and the system used to survey the site or used in the description of flora in the plan if necessary (see 1.3).

- For species, include common names if they are likely to be well known; for example in Britain, birds are usually referred to using English names, rather than scientific.

2.1
Obligations
and policies

2.2
Selection & evaluation
of the key features

2.3
Objectives, current
condition and impacts
of grazing on the
key features

2.4
Factors affecting the
management of the
key features

2.5
Rationale and
recommendations for
grazing management

2.6
Monitoring projects

2.7
Prescriptions

EXAMPLE BOX 4: Specimen Tables of Key Features

Habitat Key Features

CORINE Classification	Status	National Vegetation Classification	Birks and Ratcliffe Classification
35.1 Species rich *Nardus* grassland	HSD Priority Qualifying	CG10 *Festuca ovina-Agrostis capillaris-Thymus praecox* grassland	C1e,f Species-rich *Agrostis-Festuca*
		CG11 *F. ovina-A. capillaris-Alchemilla alpina* grassland	C1d *Alchemilla-Festuca* grassland
37.8 Eutrophic tall herbs	HSD Qualifying	U17 *Luzula sylvatica-Geum rivale* tall herb	D1 *Sedum rosea-Alchemilla glabra*
31.11 North Atlantic Wet heath	HSD Occurring	M15 a,b,c *Scirpus cespitosus-Erica tetralix* wet heath	H1 *Myrica gale-Molinia caerulea* mire G2a,b *Scirpus cespitosus-E. tetralix* mire G3 *Molinia caerulea-C. vulgaris* mire

HSD: Habitat and Species Directive

Plant Species Key Features

Species

Plants	RDB	NS	W & A	BAP
Carex lachenalii hare's-foot sedge	*			*
Potentilla crantzii alpine cinquefoil		*		
Saxifraga nivalis arctic saxifrage		*		
Saxifraga cernua drooping saxifrage	*		*	*
Bryophytes				
Arctoa fulvella		*		
Herberta borealis	*			
Lichens				
Nephroma arcticum			*	*

RDB: Red Data Book; NS: nationally scarce; W & A: Wildlife & Countryside Act 1981, Schedule 8;
BAP: Biodiversity Action Plan

2.1
Obligations and policies

2.2
Selection & evaluation of the key features

2.3
Objectives, current condition and impacts of grazing on the key features

2.4
Factors affecting the management of the key features

2.5
Rationale and recommendations for grazing management

2.6
Monitoring projects

2.7
Prescriptions

The Distribution of the Key Features at the Site

Where available, more detailed information about the key features should be included to indicate how the features occur. Details of distribution may be required to make decisions about grazing management.

Plant Community/Habitat Features

Describe how these occur at the site. This information should be site-specific and hence should be taken from surveys or other site records and could include the following:

- information on extent, distribution, altitudinal range and communities the feature tends to occur in association with

- species of note that occur within the habitat, i.e. those which have not been listed as key features but are of conservation value

Species Features

Include the following:

- details of population size, distribution, altitudinal range over which the species occurs

- for plant species, vegetation types in which the species usually occur

2.3 Objectives, Current Condition and the Impacts of Grazing

- describe what is required for each key feature; the favourable condition

- assess the current condition of each key feature in comparison with favourable condition

- discuss the predicted impacts of grazing on the key features

- describe the ideal grazing pattern to achieve favourable condition for each key feature

- assess the current impact of grazing

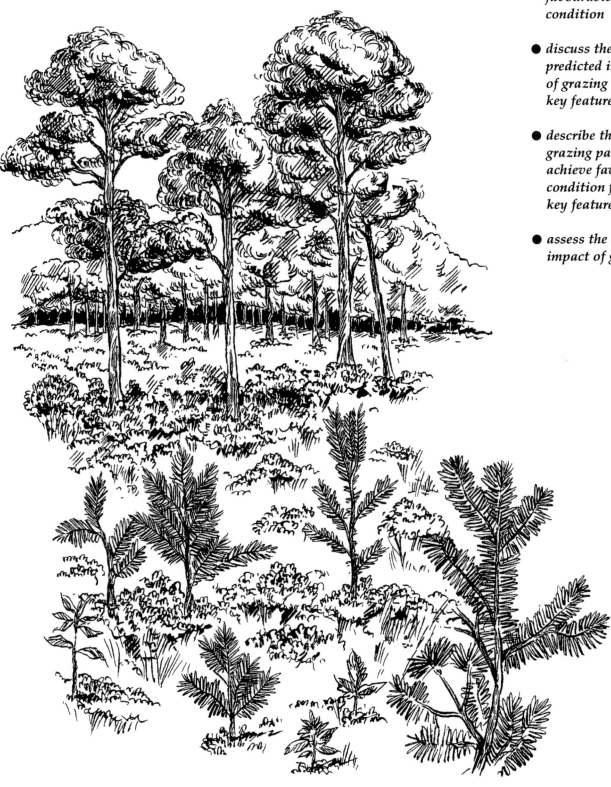

This component of the grazing plan comprises several stages which describe what is required for the key features and determine the grazing required to achieve this ideal. The plan should work through this process at the feature level; this means that the series of steps here should be presented in full for the first key feature, followed by the same procedure for the subsequent key features. The procedure is summarised below, indicating the corresponding section in the manual.

THE PROCEDURE FOR EACH KEY FEATURE

Define the objective (2.3.1)
⬇
Assess the current condition (2.3.2)
⬇
Consider the contribution of grazing to current condition (2.3.3)
⬇
Discuss the impacts of grazing and determine the ideal grazing pattern (2.3.4)

2.3.1 Defining the Objectives

The **'objective'** defines what we want of the key feature. The style of objective used in this manual is defined in Information box 3. In this manual, objectives are defined in several stages. In the most simple case, there will be an 'ideal' or 'long-term' objective which describes favourable condition (see Information box 4) of the feature. Short-term objectives may also be needed in addition to the main objective (see 'Defining Short-term Objectives'). If favourable condition cannot be defined due to a lack of information, alternative objectives will be needed as described later.

The full process for defining objectives is shown in Chart 2.1. The steps described are summarised below.

THE PROCESS FOR DEFINING OBJECTIVES

Describe favourable condition for the feature; this is the ideal or long-term objective.
⬇
Consider current condition of the feature and if necessary, add short-term objectives as described here.
⬇
If favourable condition is currently unknown, define a short-term, alternative objective.

INFORMATION BOX 3: Objectives

The objective for a feature describes what is required. The ideal, long-term objective will be to achieve favourable condition (see **Information box 4**), which is defined in terms of a **target value** and **limits of change**, for a selected range of **attributes** for the feature. Attributes are characteristics of a feature which are considered to be essential and inherent to the feature. The target value defines a specific condition which is considered to be optimal for an attribute. Limits of change set quantifiable boundaries to the attribute which, if exceeded, indicate a move into unfavourable condition. The feature is therefore, in favourable condition if the attribute is at the target value or between the limits of change. It is the limits of change for each attribute that will be used for monitoring.

Long-Term, Ideal Objectives: Defining Favourable Condition

Objectives describe the **favourable condition** of key features so that management can be implemented. Favourable condition indicates the desirable state of a feature at individual site level, rather than across a region or country. The condition of a feature at country level is known as Favourable Conservation Status and is the concern of the country agencies.

INFORMATION BOX 4: Definition of Favourable Condition for Habitats and Species

A habitat or community will be taken to be in favourable condition when:
- the area/s that it covers within the site is stable or increasing

- the specific structure and functions which are necessary for its long-term maintenance exist and are likely to continue to exist for the foreseeable future, (for dynamic seral communities the long-term maintenance of communities may be constrained by natural geomorphological and/or seral processes), and

- the condition of its typical species is favourable

A species will be taken to be in favourable condition when:
- population dynamics data on the species indicate that it is maintaining itself on a long-term basis as a viable component of its natural habitats, and

- the natural range of the species, within a site, is neither being reduced nor is likely to be reduced for the foreseeable future, and there is, and will probably continue to be, a sufficiently large habitat to maintain its population on a long-term basis.

(CCW 1996)

Every key feature should have one objective. Each objective comprises several components which together describe favourable condition of the feature. The relationship between the objective and its **attributes, target values** and **limits of change** is summarised in the box below and these terms are explained in detail below.

- **Attributes** are used to define favourable condition. They are inherent characteristics of a feature; for example, sward height and species composition of a grassland.

- The **target value** indicates the 'best' or optimal value for an attribute of the feature.

- **Limits of change** set quantifiable boundaries for the attribute which, if exceeded, indicate a move into unfavourable condition.

The purpose of this structure for the objective is to provide a set of criteria for rigorous monitoring. Attributes and limits of change set the basis for monitoring. Attributes are measured and the results are compared with the limits. The feature is in favourable condition if the attribute, when measured, is at the target value and within the limits of change.

2.1
Obligations and policies

2.2
Selection & evaluation of the key features

2.3
Objectives, current condition and impacts of grazing on the key features

2.4
Factors affecting the management of the key features

2.5
Rationale and recommendations for grazing management

2.6
Monitoring projects

2.7
Prescriptions

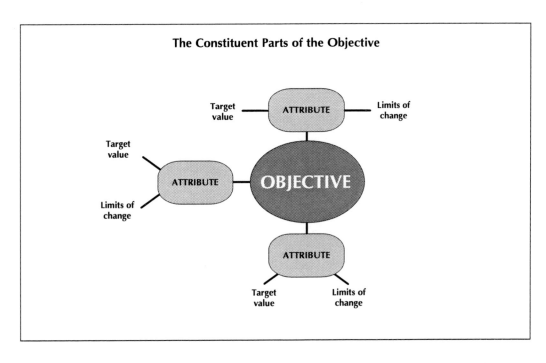

The Constituent Parts of the Objective

Selecting attributes and defining target values and limits of change requires considerable knowledge of the feature. Information and advice should be sought from staff in the country agencies, especially for features of SACs, SPAs, SSSIs and Biodiversity Action Plan or Red Data Book species. Generic guidelines which describe favourable condition for key habitat and species features in Britain are being developed by the Joint Nature Conservation Committee in conjunction with the country agencies. These guidelines are intended to be published during 1998. Expert advice can be sought from site managers, rangers (many of whom may have a long and informed knowledge of features on the site), local people, botanical recorders, ecologists, scientific resources and publications (for example, Rodwell, 1991a,b; 1992; 1995).

Attributes

Any one key feature will generally have several attributes that describe favourable condition. For habitat features, these may be:

- quantity: its area or number of discrete locations

- composition: typical desirable species; undesirable species; rare or scarce species; communities

- structure: age classes; vertical structure such as ground, shrub and tree layers; horizontal layers such as habitat fragmentation, vegetation mosaics

- physical: geological - e.g. presence of bare rock; hydrological - e.g. water table; edaphic - e.g. soil condition

Attributes for species:
- quantity: population size

- population dynamics: recruitment, mortality, emigration and immigration

- population structure: sex, age, fragmentation, isolation

- habitat requirements for feeding and breeding: area, type, structure

For each feature choose the minimum number of attributes that best describe favourable condition and/or will be useful indicators of divergence from that condition. Of the attributes listed above the two most commonly used are quantity and species composition. Information box 5 gives a selection of possible attributes for different types of vegetation feature.

INFORMATION BOX 5: Suggested Attributes for Different Vegetation Features

Feature	Attributes
Heathland	quantity; species composition such as cover of ericaceous dwarf shrubs or presence of one or more undesirable species like agricultural weeds; ratios of shrubs:graminoids & other species; tree saplings; structural attribute such as cover of different age classes of shrubs.
Grassland	quantity; species composition such as cover and frequency or abundance of one or more typical desirable species or undesirable species such as shrubs, tree saplings, weedy plant species such as thistles, rushes; physical structure of the sward such as inter-tussock height, or tussock frequency.
Woodland	quantity; percentage canopy cover of tree species; species composition such as frequency of exotic species, native species and/or rare species; age structure of the woodland, including abundance of dead wood.
Flush communities	quantity; types of NVC communities; rare species presence; percentage cover of vegetation and/or bare soil
Tall herb communities	quantity in terms of discrete locations, (although the feature may be widespread, each area tends to be very small); typical species and rare/scarce plant species.
Active blanket bog	quantity in terms of area of intact surface; cover of peat-building *sphagnum* species, presence of other important species; water table height; surface patterning.

It may be helpful to think of these questions when selecting attributes:

- In what directions might adverse change occur? Will this suggest some easily recognisable indicator? For example, frequency of tree saplings indicating successional processes in a heath.

- Are there easy positive or negative indicators of condition that would substitute for more complex measures? For example, 'weedy' species such as rushes in a herb-rich grassland, bare peat in blanket bog or species known to be good indicators of species-richness.

Target Values and Limits of Change

Each attribute is bounded by limits of change and ideally the attribute also has a **target value**. The target value describes the best possible condition and provides a starting point for setting limits of change. **Limits of change** are used because habitats and species are naturally dynamic and will fluctuate in quantity, composition and structure. The limits are designed to take account of this variation by defining the degree to which an attribute can fluctuate around a target value without giving cause for concern. In Example box 5, the target value of heathland is 380 hectares, the upper limit is 400 ha and the lower is 300 ha. Note that the target value is between, but is not necessarily mid-way between, the upper and lower limits.

2.1
Obligations and policies

2.2
Selection & evaluation of the key features

2.3
Objectives, current condition and impacts of grazing on the key features

2.4
Factors affecting the management of the key features

2.5
Rationale and recommendations for grazing management

2.6
Monitoring projects

2.7
Prescriptions

EXAMPLE BOX 5: Attributes, Targets and Limits of Change for Heathland

Attribute	Upper limit	Target value	Lower limit
Quantity	400 ha	380 ha	300 ha
Species composition: ground cover of dwarf shrubs *Calluna vulgaris*, & *Erica cinerea*	90% cover	80% cover	60% cover
Frequency of tree saplings above shrub canopy	40% frequency	No saplings above canopy	None

EXAMPLE BOX 6: Objective for a Grazed Grassland

Objective: To maintain the CG10 *Festuca ovina-Agrostis capillaris-Thymus praecox* grassland in favourable condition where:

Attribute	Upper limit	Target value	Lower limit
Quantity	none	increasing	no reduction in area through anthropogenic impacts
Species composition	no upper limit to small-herb species-richness	The following species present as constants: *Campanula rotundifolia*, *Carex capillaris*, *Linum catharticum*, *Plantago maritima*, *Prunella vulgaris*, *Thymus praecox*, *Viola riviniana*.	no fewer than 6 of the species listed in the target, present as constants
Structure: summer inter-tussock mean sward height	10 cm	5 cm	3 cm
Tree saplings	<5/10 ha	No saplings present	None

Limits should be set so that they are reached some time before there is a significant threat to the viability of a feature. The limits are a trigger so that if exceeded the site manager will be alerted to investigate well before the point of irrevocable change is reached. In this respect, the target value can indicate trends, i.e. the direction in which the attribute is moving with respect to the target value. Limits can be set close to the desired thresholds, as in the above case and the example below for sward heights, when the dynamics of a feature are well understood and are therefore predictable.

To monitor a feature, the target value and the limits of change for the attributes should be measurable. It is also important that they are ecologically realistic and not guesses. In Example box 6 a range of plant species is given for the target value and limits of change and the sward height is set at levels known to maintain the diversity of small herb species by reducing competition from shrubs or aggressive grasses.

However, quantitative targets and limits may be difficult to define, either because of lack of reliable information or because of the nature of the feature. In Example box 6 the exact area is not specified because the boundaries of this type of species-rich grassland are difficult to measure since they occur in a mosaic with other grassland communities. The limits and target condition for quantity are therefore defined in a qualitative manner and monitoring can be targeted at parts of the boundary where change is expected to take place.

2.1
Obligations and policies

2.2
Selection & evaluation of the key features

2.3
Objectives, current condition and impacts of grazing on the key features

2.4
Factors affecting the management of the key features

2.5
Rationale and recommendations for grazing management

2.6
Monitoring projects

2.7
Prescriptions

When thinking about targets and limits of change, it may be helpful to ask these questions:

- Are the attributes measurable?

- How much of something is desirable; how high can the limit be either ecologically or before it starts to conflict with another feature?

- How little of something is desirable; how low can the limit be before its viability is threatened?

- How is the attribute to be monitored, i.e. what are the practical problems of monitoring the feature?

For the feature to be in favourable condition and the objective achieved, all the attributes, which taken together give an overall picture of the feature, should meet or be moving towards the target values. The limits to the attribute act as 'flashing lights' that alert a site manager to undesired changes. This initiates a process of assessing the causes so that management can be changed where necessary.

The manual has so far described how to define favourable condition. The following sections consider circumstances in which it is not possible or sufficient to have an objective for favourable condition.

Short-Term Objectives

If the assessment of current condition (2.3.2) indicates that a key feature is unfavourable and it needs to be restored, this may have to be built into the objective for the feature if the restoration process exceeds the time period covered by the grazing plan. This situation will cause difficulties for monitoring because in the short-term, the feature will continue to fail to meet the criteria for favourable condition, even if it is improving as a result of management. In these cases, short-term objectives should be developed, to determine if restoration is working. These short-term objectives should be indicators of progress towards favourable condition. Short-term objectives can be included as time-limited attributes within the long-term objective; simply add attributes that are indicators of the success of restoration work and note the time period which these objectives cover. Ensure that in the short-term, monitoring projects record these restoration attributes.

As an example of a feature which requires restoration, consider a woodland currently comprised of over-mature trees of one species with no regeneration, little seed production by existing trees and heavy grazing pressure exerted by wild red deer. The aim of restoration may be to regenerate a mixed-species woodland. A definition of favourable condition for the woodland could include attributes such as:

- age structure

- density of trees

- species mix

- successful regeneration

Management for restoration would include planting some species, relying on seed rain for other species and gradually reducing the grazing pressure by culling the deer. These processes will take time and the development of a woodland which meets the favourable condition criteria is not likely to occur within the life of the average grazing plan, of say five years. A short-term objective would set short-term targets which would indicate that management was working and the woodland was

2.1
Obligations and policies

2.2
Selection & evaluation of the key features

2.3
Objectives, current condition and impacts of grazing on the key features

2.4
Factors affecting the management of the key features

2.5
Rationale and recommendations for grazing management

2.6
Monitoring projects

2.7
Prescriptions

moving towards favourable condition. Attributes for this objective might include the following:

- the survival rate of planted trees

- the height of planted trees

- seed production in planted trees as they mature

These attributes would indicate whether the planting programme was successful and whether deer culling was proving beneficial. The attributes should be included in the objective, with limits of change and targets and an indication of the time period over which they should be monitored in place of the long-term attributes that describe favourable condition.

Alternative Objectives

So far a process has been described for writing an ideal, long-term objective that defines favourable condition. In some cases, it will not be possible to define favourable condition using attributes and limits of change because of a lack of information; for example if a generic definition has not been prepared by the statutory agency and there is limited knowledge of the feature. In this case, it will not be possible to produce an ideal, long-term objective and there will be no criteria against which to assess current or future condition. For the purposes of the plan, develop an alternative objective as follows:

- Record an 'Information Project' in the plan which notes the need to gather more information to define favourable condition in consultation with the statutory agency, when information is available.

- Write an objective which aims to ensure that there is no loss of condition before favourable condition is defined. An example of such an objective would be 'to avoid change or deterioration of the feature in the short-term' using attributes based on the state of the feature at present.

2.3.2 Assessing Current Condition

This section includes the following:
- a definition of current condition

- how to assess current condition

- alternative methods when information is lacking

The current condition of a key feature is an assessment of whether the feature meets the criteria for favourable condition set out in the objective. This means that current condition can only be fully described if favourable condition has been defined for the objective (see 'Assessments of Vegetation or Habitat Condition' below for other methods).

The process is shown within Chart 2.1 (page 35). Assess current condition for each of the key features for which there is a set of attributes with limits of change defining favourable condition.

To assess current condition
Follow the process summarised in the box below.

The assessment of current condition is used as an indicator of whether a change to the current management is required; if the feature is in unfavourable condition, management will need to be reviewed. Note that current condition is not the same as the impact of grazing (see Information box 5) and it should not be assumed that inappropriate grazing is the cause of unfavourable condition. The assessment of the impact of grazing is described later (2.3.3 'The Influence of the Current Grazing Regime on Condition').

INFORMATION BOX 5: Current Condition cf. Impacts of Grazing

It is crucial to understand the difference between assessments of **current condition** and the **impacts of grazing**. Current condition is used as an indicator of whether a change in management is required to meet the objective for a feature. The condition of a feature is influenced by a range of factors, of which grazing is just one. So, if a feature is unfavourable, it does not follow that a change to the grazing regime is required. This should prompt an investigation into the range of factors that have an impact on the feature, to find out why it is unfavourable. An assessment of the current impact of grazing on the feature would be made as part of this investigation to determine the role of grazing. Only then can changes to grazing management be proposed.

Assessments of Vegetation or Habitat Condition

If favourable condition has not been defined using attributes with limits of change, it will not be possible to determine current condition as described because there are no criteria against which to compare any measurements of the vegetation. However, alternative, less rigorous assessments can be made in the meantime. There are a few options available for certain plant communities for sites in Britain, which either provide indicators of condition or describe the relationship between impacts and condition. These methods are discussed in Appendix 10.

2.3.3 The Influence of the Current Grazing Regime on Condition

Following the assessment of current condition, for features found to be in unfavourable condition, it is essential to determine the cause. Grazing is only one of several potential causes. For the purposes of a grazing plan, it is necessary to determine whether grazing management should be changed to meet the objective for the feature. This procedure is included in the process shown in Chart 2.1.

Methods for assessing the impact of grazing on vegetation have been developed by Scottish Natural Heritage and English Nature. These and other sources of information are described in Appendix 10. Such methods should be used to determine whether current grazing regimes are appropriate for vegetation types that appear as key features, or are important habitats for animal species listed as key features.

2.3.4 The Impacts of Grazing on the Key Features and Ideal Grazing Patterns

- a discussion of current knowledge on the ecological impacts of various possible grazing regimes on each key feature

- a description of the 'ideal grazing pattern' for each key feature

Content and Purpose

This section of the plan comprises a discussion of the ecological impacts of grazing on the key features. The main purpose is to determine the pattern of grazing which will best meet the objectives for each key feature; this is referred to as the 'ideal grazing pattern' (see Information box 6). The result will be to present in the plan an ideal grazing pattern for each key feature. This is the first step in deciding how the objectives could be achieved via grazing management. The present section of the manual provides guidance on how to assess the impact of grazing on vegetation and write the discussion for a grazing plan.

2.1
Obligations
and policies

2.2
Selection & evaluation
of the key features

2.3
Objectives, current
condition and impacts
of grazing on the
key features

2.4
Factors affecting the
management of the
key features

2.5
Rationale and
recommendations for
grazing management

2.6
Monitoring projects

2.7
Prescriptions

INFORMATION BOX 6: The Ideal Grazing Pattern for a Key Feature

An **'ideal grazing pattern'** for a key feature defines what pattern of grazing is needed to maintain the feature as described in the objective. This pattern includes the timing and pressure of grazing which would best achieve the objective, but does not define stocking densities or herbivore species. It may also be useful to specify the degree of selectivity in grazing for some features. For example, some vegetation types may benefit from non-selective grazing and this should be considered when selecting the appropriate grazing animal. For further information on grazing patterns see Information box 2 (page 32).

How to Determine the Impact of Grazing on Key Features

In order to describe the impact of grazing on a key feature, collate and summarise existing knowledge about the impacts of grazing animals, using this section of the manual as a guide. For those features which are poorly understood, identify gaps in the existing knowledge, so that this may be considered later as a factor affecting the management of the key features. The different types of key feature should be treated as follows:

■ For habitat/plant community features, discuss the impacts of grazing as described. Sources of information for sites in Britain include Jerram and Drewitt (1998), Rodwell (1991a, 1991b, 1992, 1995) and MacDonald et al. (1998).

■ For animal species features, requirements in terms of habitat/food plant/habitat for prey species should be discussed, and the impacts of grazing on the vegetation which provides these requirements should then be dealt with as described for plant communities.

■ For plant species features, use published information of the impacts of grazing where available.

In the discussion for each vegetation type/habitat, follow the guidance in the boxes below and use Chart 2.2 for information on the factors which determine the impact of grazing on vegetation.

FOR EACH KEY FEATURE CONSIDER THE FOLLOWING QUESTIONS:

■ What are the predicted impacts of broad categories of grazing pressure, such as 'high', 'moderate' and 'low'?

■ What are the predicted impacts of variations in the seasonal pattern of grazing?

■ Can grazing have both positive and negative impacts, depending on the regime applied?

■ What are the impacts of trampling and poaching, particularly on the structure of the vegetation?

■ How preferred is the vegetation in question compared with other types present, i.e. how likely are the herbivores to graze it? Consider this in relation to the foraging behaviour of the particular herbivore species present at the site, or of species that could occur in the future.

ANSWER THE QUESTIONS IN TERMS OF THE FOLLOWING IMPACTS:

■ Consider impacts of grazing in terms of direct effects on survival, growth and reproductive capacity of individual species.

■ Consider the impact of grazing on species composition of the vegetation.

■ Note the effect of grazing on species of particular importance, such as those which are selectively grazed or avoided, and those of high nature conservation value.

■ Consider how grazing affects the attributes used to define objectives for plant community features.

2.1
Obligations
and policies

2.2
Selection & evaluation
of the key features

2.3
Objectives, current
condition and impacts
of grazing on the
key features

2.4
Factors affecting the
management of the
key features

2.5
Rationale and
recommendations for
grazing management

2.6
Monitoring projects

2.7
Prescriptions

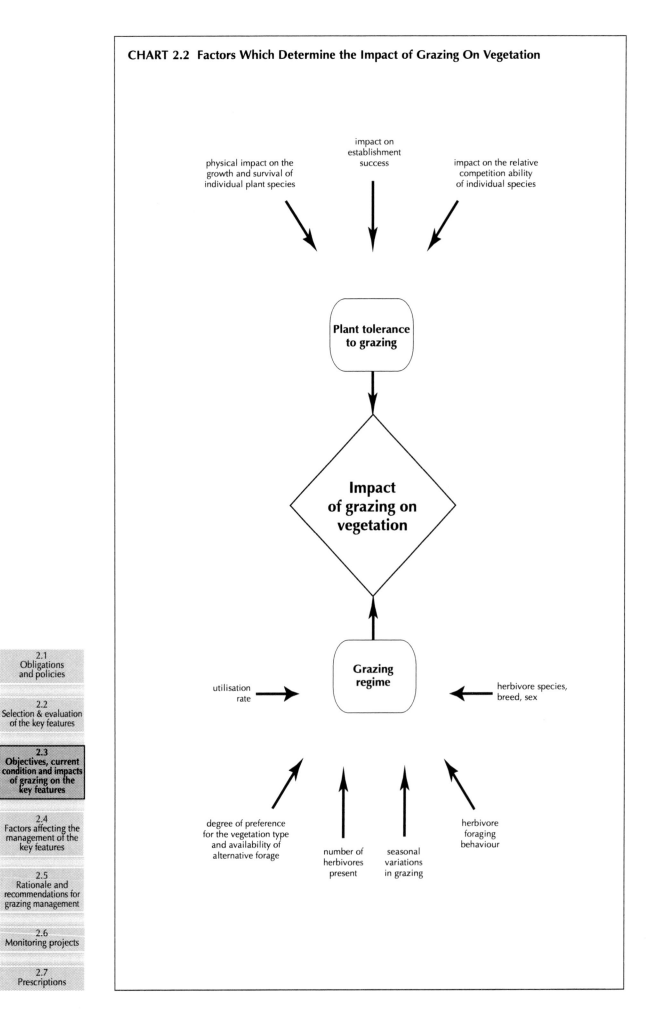

CHART 2.2 Factors Which Determine the Impact of Grazing On Vegetation

physical impact on the growth and survival of individual plant species

impact on establishment success

impact on the relative competition ability of individual species

Plant tolerance to grazing

Impact of grazing on vegetation

utilisation rate

Grazing regime

herbivore species, breed, sex

degree of preference for the vegetation type and availability of alternative forage

number of herbivores present

seasonal variations in grazing

herbivore foraging behaviour

2.1
Obligations and policies

2.2
Selection & evaluation of the key features

2.3
Objectives, current condition and impacts of grazing on the key features

2.4
Factors affecting the management of the key features

2.5
Rationale and recommendations for grazing management

2.6
Monitoring projects

2.7
Prescriptions

The impact of grazing on plant communities depends on how the species within the community respond to grazing as shown in Chart 2.2. Further details of utilisation rate, the importance of herbivore foraging behaviour, plant tolerance to grazing are given in Information boxes 7 - 9 and Appendices 6, 7, 8,12.

INFORMATION BOX 7: Herbivore Foraging Patterns and Predictions of Impact

In general, selective herbivore species will choose to graze vegetation types of highest nutritional value first and their use of other vegetation will depend on the availability of preferred vegetation. There is a basic order of preference which applies to most selective herbivore species, but this varies with season (see Appendices 6, 7, 8 for more information on individual species). Note also that herbivores can choose only from the vegetation available at the site, so foraging behaviour will depend on the range of vegetation and will be site-specific to some degree.

Highly preferred vegetation types will usually be most heavily grazed of the available vegetation and other vegetation types will tend to be grazed much less until the preferred type has been depleted. This means that the availability of preferred vegetation affects the grazing pressure on other types. Availability varies with site and with herbivore density so a reduction in herbivore densities may not reduce the grazing pressure on preferred vegetation types; grazing pressure on the less nutritional vegetation will decline first.

Vegetation types of poor forage value will generally be avoided by selective animals. This vegetation may not be grazed at all, unless herbivore densities are very high and/or the availability of good quality forage is low.

It should be possible to predict, depending on the vegetation types present at a site, which types will be most and least heavily grazed at different times of year. This is easiest for the extreme examples mentioned: communities that are either highly favoured or mostly avoided. However, there are 'intermediate' communities which are neither strongly preferred nor selectively avoided and utilisation of these vegetation types will fluctuate considerably with the availability of preferred vegetation, and hence with herbivore numbers. It is difficult to predict how much these communities will be grazed with different densities of animals.

INFORMATION BOX 8: Utilisation Rate

The proportion of the annual vegetation production removed by grazing animals. Utilisation rate is a strong determinant of impact.

INFORMATION BOX 9: Tolerance to Grazing

Individual plant species and plant communities vary in their tolerance or response to grazing, due to direct impacts on the reproductive success, growth and survival of species and also to indirect impacts on the relative competitive ability of the species within communities. For example, grass species tend to be highly tolerant to grazing, while small herbs can be easily damaged when grazing inhibits flowering and growth.

2.1
Obligations
and policies

2.2
Selection & evaluation
of the key features

2.3
Objectives, current
condition and impacts
of grazing on the
key features

2.4
Factors affecting the
management of the
key features

2.5
Rationale and
recommendations for
grazing management

2.6
Monitoring projects

2.7
Prescriptions

Describing The Ideal Grazing Pattern

It should now be possible, from the information collated, to determine an ideal grazing pattern for the key feature, which is expected to meet the objectives for the feature. Compile as detailed a description as possible of this pattern in terms of: grazing pressure, timing, the degree of selectivity required. For some features, there will be a lack of scientific information and it may be possible to make only general conclusions, such as 'some' grazing required.

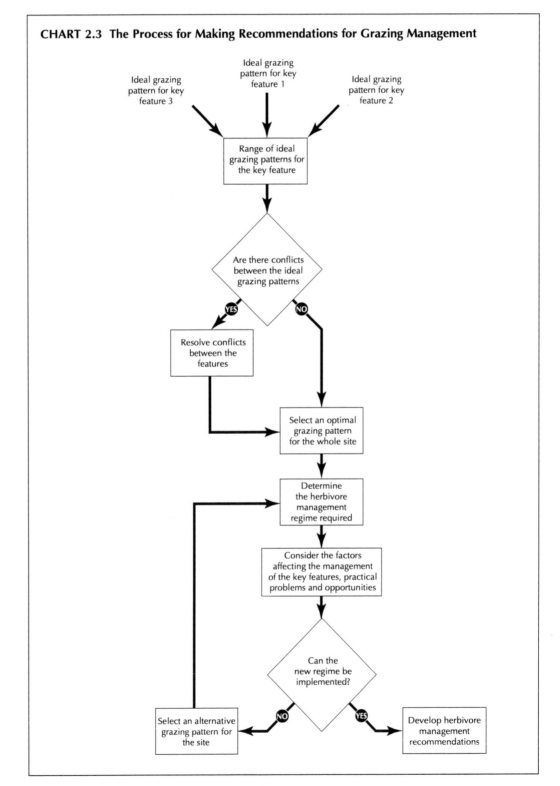

CHART 2.3 The Process for Making Recommendations for Grazing Management

Ideal grazing pattern for key feature 1

Ideal grazing pattern for key feature 3

Ideal grazing pattern for key feature 2

Range of ideal grazing patterns for the key feature

Are there conflicts between the ideal grazing patterns

YES — Resolve conflicts between the features

NO

Select an optimal grazing pattern for the whole site

Determine the herbivore management regime required

Consider the factors affecting the management of the key features, practical problems and opportunities

Can the new regime be implemented?

NO — Select an alternative grazing pattern for the site

YES — Develop herbivore management recommendations

2.1
Obligations and policies

2.2
Selection & evaluation of the key features

**2.3
Objectives, current condition and impacts of grazing on the key features**

2.4
Factors affecting the management of the key features

2.5
Rationale and recommendations for grazing management

2.6
Monitoring projects

2.7
Prescriptions

CASE STUDY: 2.3 Objective, Current Condition and Influence of Grazing

2.3.1 Objective for Grazed Grassland.

To maintain Species-rich *Nardus* grassland (Corine 35.1) NVC CG10 *Festuca ovina-Agrostis capillaris-Thymus praecox* and CG11 *Festuca ovina-Alchemilla alpina* grasslands in favourable condition, where:

For CG10

Attribute	Upper limit	Target value	Lower limit
Quantity	no limit unless threatening other habitats	increasing unless at the expense of other important habitats	no reduction in the current area of the habitat through anthropogenic impacts
Species composition:	no upper limit to small-herb species-richness	within a floristically homogenous area the following species present as constants: *Campanula rotundifolia, Carex capillaris, Linum carthaticum, Plantago maritima, Prunella vulgaris, Thymus praecox, Viola riviniana.*	not less than 6 of the species listed in the target, present as constants in a floristically homogenous area
Structure: summer inter-tussock mean sward height	10 cm	5 cm	3 cm
Tree saplings	<5/10 ha	No saplings present	None set

For CG11

Alternative Objective: To avoid deterioration of CG11 from current condition where:

Attribute	Upper limit	Target value	Lower limit
Quantity	no limit unless threatening other habitats	None set	no reduction in the current area of the habitat through anthropogenic impacts
Species composition:	no upper limit to small-herb species-richness	within a floristically homogenous area the following species present as constants: *Alchemilla alpina, Galium saxatile, Hylocomium splendens, Potentilla erecta, Thymus praecox, Vaccinum myrtillus*	Not less than 4 of the species listed in the target
Structure: summer inter-tussock mean sward height	15 cm	None set	5 cm
Tree saplings	<5/10 ha	No saplings present	None set

2.1
Obligations
and policies

2.2
Selection & evaluation
of the key features

2.3
**Objectives, current
condition and impacts
of grazing on the
key features**

2.4
Factors affecting the
management of the
key features

2.5
Rationale and
recommendations for
grazing management

2.6
Monitoring projects

2.7
Prescriptions

2.3.2 Current Condition

No systematic assessment of current condition has been carried out for the two NVC communities comprising this Annex 1 habitat. Favourable condition has recently been defined for CG10, but for CG11 favourable condition has yet to be finalised. In this case, an interim objective has been set based on a typical CG11 description (Rodwell 1992), rather than a site-specific definition. The current condition is unknown for CG11 but for CG10 the grazing impacts survey measured some attributes which have subsequently been used to define favourable condition. The results of this have been used to make a tentative assessment of current condition as being favourable under the current grazing regime (2.3.3 see below).

2.3.3 Influence of the Current Grazing Regime

CG10 grassland: The most important area of this habitat occurs on unit III. An assessment of grazing levels and other impacts was carried out in September 1996 on this unit and during this survey sward height was measured, presence of tree saplings was recorded and species representative of typical CG10 grassland were checked (see Appendix 1 of site Grazing Plan).

Within the 79 hectares of CG10 grassland, sward structure and species composition is inherently variable due to the great variation in geologic and edaphic conditions on these steep slopes (see 2.2). Where grazed, the sward is smooth, with average inter-tussock sward height between 3 cm-6 cm especially on the lower slopes below the cliffs. The sward height is therefore within the limits of change. Typical (Rodwell 1992) CG10 species (which did not include the site scarcity, *Carex capillaris* nor the less typical but important on this site, *Plantago maritima*) were present in 75% of samples but species composition was sampled for only 3 quadrats and in these the target species were within the limits specified above. Species numbers in these quadrats averaged thirty-one. Tree saplings were sometimes locally abundant in the sward but over the whole area of CG10 grassland the frequency of saplings is less than 5%.

The dominant impact on the CG10 is year-round grazing by Blackface ewes plus lambs and hoggs in summer. Red deer are infrequent, roe deer are occasionally seen coming out from the neighbouring coniferous forest but compared to the sheep, their contributions to grazing impact is negligible. Although the extent of the CG10 would need to be remapped to compare with the previous area and further quadrat data for species composition is required, the presence of typical species in the majority of samples, the sward height and infrequency of tree saplings generally indicate that the current grazing regime appears to be maintaining this feature in acceptable condition.

CG11 grassland: The CG11 occurs as small patches throughout the *Agostis-Festuca* dominated sward. Where *Alchemilla alpina* appears it is prominent whilst *Thymus praecox* is scarce but other small forbs which are common in acid grasslands occur patchily throughout. A brief visual examination of grazing impacts was carried out in July 1996 when grazing was assessed to be light with some more moderately grazed patches. Species composition and sward height are very variable at a small scale. This unit was grazed by about 200 Blackface sheep until the flock was removed in early 1996. Deer are known to use the area also and increasing numbers are thought to have moved onto this grassland since the removal of the sheep, but the impact deer are having is unknown.

Information Projects

1. Collect further quadrat data for CG10 grassland to determine species composition over the whole habitat.

2. Define favourable condition of CG11

3. Survey and carry out current condition survey of CG11 when the objective for favourable condition has been determined.

2.3.4 Impacts of Grazing and Ideal Grazing Pattern

The following generalised information for CG10 and CG11 is taken largely from Rodwell (1992). Both CG10 and CG11 are plagioclimax communities probably derived from ash or oak/birch woodland at low altitudes or *Dryas* heath at higher altitudes. Both are anthro

(Objective, Current Condition and Influence of Grazing - continued)

pogenic habitats usually sought out and normally maintained by herbivores, usually now sheep, with variable influence from deer and other wild herbivores. These communities generally occur as small areas in mosaics with other grazed grasslands. The closed swards are dominated by palatable grasses with very variable amounts of *Nardus*. The swards are often rich in light demanding small-herb species and perennial hemicrypto-phytes which survive as tight rosettes. Species-richness and abundance is strongly influenced by the degree of flushing. Bryophytes can be conspicuous in CG11 swards and tall herbs may also be present although reduced in stature by grazing.

Too heavy and too light levels of grazing, especially in CG10, will reduce species richness. In the former case heavy grazing suppresses the fine grasses and small herbs, allows the bryophyte cover to increase and more unpalatable or grazing resistant species such as *Alchemilla alpina*, *Prunella vulgaris*, and *Cirscium* spp. to become more abundant. If grazing becomes too light, tussocky grasses, tall herbs if present and dwarf shrubs such as *Calluna vulgaris* or *Vaccinium myrtillus* will eventually out-compete the small herbs. Removal of all grazing would allow succession to ash/oak woodland, especially for the CG10 on unit III where there are plentiful neighbouring seed sources and there was evidence of seedlings below the cliffs. Scattered woodland might also develop eventually on the CG11 on unit IV as seeds spread from more distant sources.

These grasslands on this site are preferred areas of grazing. The CG10, especially with increasing altitude up the steep hillside, occurs in small-scale mosaics with very lightly grazed tussock grass species such as *Nardus stricta* and *Molinia caerulea* whilst the fine grasses, especially *Agrostis* and *Festuca* species are highly preferred. Little is known about the effects of grazing on individual plant species but from observation it appears that *Thymus praecox* is maintained in small clumps on the shortest swards, but survives by straggling through taller swards. and possibly grazing limits its spread. Less palatable species such as *Prunella vulgaris* are more abundant in the shortest swards. *Carex capillaris* is associated with more open or short swards and in September there was ample evidence of seed heads. In CG11 *Alchemilla alpina* appears to be avoided by herbivores but it is expected that the same grasses will be preferred grazing as for CG10.

The ideal grazing pattern should aim to be moderate to high grazing pressures which reduces competition from dwarf shrub and tussocky graminoid species, suppresses tree colonisation and maintains a short, open sward where light levels are high and small herb species can flourish. The grazing pattern may be year-round, but there is consid-erable evidence from lowland sites in England, and coastal sites in Scotland, that a seasonal regime can benefit species-rich grasslands. Cessation of grazing over the summer allows flowering and seeding of small herbs which replenishes and re-invigorates the populations. This should be followed by heavy grazing in autumn and winter when the forbs are dormant, to remove the graminoid biomass, open up the sward to allow germination of forbs and to suppress dwarf shrubs. Little is known of the dynamics of these grasslands in upland regions under the environmental constraints such as occur on this site.

2.1
Obligations
and policies

2.2
Selection & evaluation
of the key features

2.3
Objectives, current
condition and impacts
of grazing on the
key features

2.4
Factors affecting the
management of the
key features

2.5
Rationale and
recommendations for
grazing management

2.6
Monitoring projects

2.7
Prescriptions

2.4 Factors Affecting the Management of the Key Features

- *describe practical constraints on the options for management*

- *discuss opportunities for achieving the desired grazing management*

- *identify conflicts of interest between conservation and other factors*

Content and Purpose

In this component of the plan, the discussion returns to the whole-site level. 'Factors affecting the management of the key features' (referred to here as 'factors') are also called 'opportunities and constraints' in management plans or planning guides. In this section of the plan, describe the range of factors that determine how a key feature or the whole site may be managed. For grazing plans it is necessary to describe only factors relevant to grazing management. Factors can be:

- positive or negative in terms of their influence on the management options

- related to the practicalities of managing the site; such as lack of resources, conflicting policies of landowners or the degree of control over grazing

- biological requirements of the features; for example if an animal species is the feature, its habitat, in terms of the vegetation to be managed, would be a factor

- biological processes, such as succession or regeneration, which need to be considered or managed

- a lack of knowledge about the site, the features, the herbivores etc.

- physical aspects of the feature or site that need to be noted but cannot be managed, for example, hydrology on a bog

- designations for the site

2.4.1 How to Compile the List of Factors

Information collated for preceding parts of the plan, particularly the Description, should be used to compile a list of factors. Discuss the implications of each factor for the management of the site or for individual key features, and indicate whether the effect on management is positive or negative if relevant. Problems associated with the factors should not be resolved in this section, they should only be described. Factors most likely to be relevant to a grazing plan are discussed below; the number in brackets indicates the plan component in which the original details are included.

Tenure and Owners'/Occupiers' Objectives (1.5)
Consider the interests and land management practices of the current owners and occupiers of the site. These may conflict with the stated nature conservation objectives and therefore

have a potential negative impact on the options for management. For example, an owner may wish to maximise the cover of grass-dominated vegetation as forage for his stock on a site where heath is cited as a key feature. Conversely, the objectives of the owner may include nature conservation and this is a factor with a positive influence.

Grazing Rights/Tenancies (1.5)
If there are legal agreements permitting stock grazing on the site, the options for changing current limits should be discussed. For example, if there is a tenant sheep farmer who wishes to maximise sheep numbers on his tenancy this could limit the options for changing the numbers of grazing animals. The discussion should interpret the details such as the nature of the tenancy agreement to indicate how strongly this factor will influence decisions made about grazing

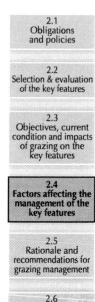

2.1
Obligations
and policies

2.2
Selection & evaluation
of the key features

2.3
Objectives, current
condition and impacts
of grazing on the
key features

2.4
Factors affecting the
management of the
key features

2.5
Rationale and
recommendations for
grazing management

2.6
Monitoring projects

2.7
Prescriptions

management. If agreements include long-term, legal rights to graze a given number of animals, this limits the options for changing the current stocking rate, unless supported by financial incentives.

Knowledge of Current Grazing Animals (1.3; 1.5)

Information on the current numbers and distribution of herbivores is presented in the 'Description'. The quantity and quality of the information available influences the accuracy of predictions which can be made about the effects of herbivores on the features. If there is little information, or if details are based on assumptions or poor estimates, it is more difficult to make the link between grazing patterns and the condition of the vegetation for the site. This creates problems when trying to determine what a more appropriate number of herbivores might be. Describe any gaps in knowledge as factors and explain where estimates have been made.

Herbivore Foraging Patterns

Herbivore foraging behaviour will be a factor because most species are selective to some degree, although this varies between species. This can be an advantage, for example in the management of plagioclimax grassland communities. These require grazing to maintain them, and they are likely to be preferentially grazed. The broad foraging patterns of the herbivore species present should be discussed in relation to the vegetation present.

Information on Grazing Resource (1.3)

Any gaps in knowledge of the distribution and extent of vegetation should be discussed here. This will influence the accuracy with which predictions of grazing behaviour can be made and will also limit the accuracy of management proposals.

Physical Features (1.2)

Important geological, geomorphological, historical or archaeological features at the site can influence the options for grazing management. The status of such features should be noted in the Description, but the implications for management and any conflicts with the objectives of the grazing plan should be discussed here. For example, if there is an objective to restore woodland, this may conflict with archaeological features. The status of such features will determine their priority, relative to the key features of the grazing plan.

Recreation (1.2; 1.5; 2.1)

Any conflicts between current recreational use and the objectives should be discussed. For example, if access is important, this may put constraints upon options for erecting fences to control herbivore movements. Heavy visitor pressure may also limit the options for culling; both in terms of the potential danger to visitors and also the disturbance to animals caused by visitors which can influence the distribution of species such as deer.

Biological Features (1.3)

There may be biological features of interest that were not selected as key features and therefore are not included in the objectives. This situation would arise if these other features were not regarded as being of equal priority to the key features. However, these features can be considered in the grazing plan by treating them as factors. In this case, the features should be mentioned and knowledge of their ideal grazing regimes may be summarised so that the impact on these additional features of proposed grazing regimes for the site can be discussed in 2.5 'Rationale and Recommendations for Grazing Management'.

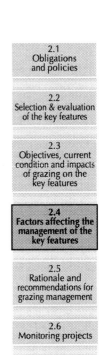

2.1
Obligations
and policies

2.2
Selection & evaluation
of the key features

2.3
Objectives, current
condition and impacts
of grazing on the
key features

**2.4
Factors affecting the
management of the
key features**

2.5
Rationale and
recommendations for
grazing management

2.6
Monitoring projects

2.7
Prescriptions

Knowledge of the Key Features (2.3)

There may be a lack of a clear definition of favourable condition for some of the features, so objectives will be incomplete. This should be discussed here because decisions about grazing management are likely to be short-term and will change as further information becomes available.

Conflicting Objectives (2.3)

The discussion of grazing impacts for each of the key features may have revealed a direct conflict between some of the features in terms of the ideal grazing pattern required to maintain them. This is an important factor.

Practical Animal Management (1.5)

This covers a wide range of possible factors. Consider the ideal grazing patterns suggested in 2.3 and determine any immediate constraints on achieving them which so far have not been covered. Particularly consider any practical restrictions on managing herbivores, such as moving them to influence distribution or introducing new stock. For example, if summer rest would benefit certain features but there is no alternative summer grazing for stock, this is a factor. The presence of free-ranging wild herbivores, such as red deer, will also be a factor to consider. There are practical difficulties associated with controlling the number and distribution of these animals which do not apply to the management of domestic herbivores.

Biological Processes (2.3)

Biological processes should have been mentioned in the discussion of 'grazing impacts' as trends associated with different grazing patterns. For example, a lightly grazed heath may be threatened by succession to woodland as a result of natural regeneration if seed sources are present. The potential effect of succession should be discussed here, noting that it is a problem to consider when developing the grazing regime.

Equally, the importance of regeneration for woodland features should be discussed. In this case, regeneration will be a positive factor, provided there is no invasion by exotic species, and this will contribute to the maintenance of the woodland. Regeneration may be limited by poor availability of seeds and/or germination niches and this should be discussed.

Availability of Resources

The implementation of management recommendations is likely to cost money. Resources will be limited and this is an important factor, constraining the range of options for changing the current management practices.

Obligations, Designations and Policies (1.2; 2.1)

The restrictions imposed by any policies or designations described in 2.1 should be discussed, with specific details of the way in which they may influence management.

Community Objectives/Public Interest

Some sites may have particular value to the local community in the area; for example a site may be valued for its openness. This should be described if there is likely to be conflict with such interest and the objectives of the management plan.

Socio-Economic Concerns

The social aspects of agriculture or other land-uses on the site must be considered, particularly in rural communities dependent on such land-use. There may be conflicts between proposed management for nature conservation and the economics of the local community.

CASE STUDY: 2.4 Factors Affecting the Management of the Key Features

2.4.1 Lack of Knowledge

In order to make informed decisions about the appropriate stocking regime for Ben Lawers, ideally information is needed on the number and distribution of the major herbivores, the distribution of habitats, grazing pressure on each habitat and the impact of grazing on these habitats.

Little is known about the distribution and foraging behaviour of sheep and deer on the cSAC. There are some records of the overall level of grazing on some patches of different habitats (Life Project Habitat Condition Assessment of 1996), but this is limited to only three habitats and little is known about how grazing pressure varies spatially across the site. In addition, the relative contribution of deer and sheep to this grazing pressure is unknown and the interactions between the two species are poorly understood. For example, a reduction in the number of sheep may not reduce grazing pressure on preferred habitats because deer may increase their use of these vegetation types. Both species may need to be managed but in the current situation, it is difficult to determine how each should be managed. In practical terms, it is more difficult to control the spatial and temporal distribution of deer, than it is to control sheep.

To supplement existing information, predictions can be made about the vegetation types which sheep and deer would be most likely to graze. The accuracy of these predictions however, depends on information on the distribution of animals. Furthermore, any predictions will be most accurate for highly preferred vegetation such as the herb-rich grassland, or for vegetation types which have poor forage value, such as bogs. Vegetation types with a high forage value will always be preferentially grazed, while communities of very low nutritional quality will be grazed only when the availability of preferred types is low. It is more difficult to predict how heavily vegetation types of intermediate forage value will be grazed. As preferred vegetation becomes depleted, animals will begin to graze other types, or increase their use of these types. Very poor forage will still be avoided and utilisation of the vegetation of intermediate forage value will vary most, depending on herbivore numbers and even on annual variations in weather. The alpine pioneer (flush) communities at Ben Lawers are of intermediate forage value and there is observational evidence to suggest that this vegetation tends to be grazed more in dry summers than in other years; indicating how variable grazing pressure on this community is. Availability depends not only on the extent of preferred vegetation types at the site, but also on the density of herbivores; the higher the density, the greater the grazing pressure, which means that preferred vegetation will be quickly depleted. Clearly it is difficult to predict accurately how heavily different vegetation types will be grazed and any predictions should be used with extreme care.

The relationship between grazing pressure and impact on vegetation condition is also poorly understood; there is some scientific information for certain plant communities, but the results tend to be site-specific. As a result, it is difficult to accurately determine the timing, pressure and selectivity of grazing required for each habitat.

These factors combine to make it difficult to develop proposals for herbivore management because the ideal grazing pattern for each habitat is not clearly known and the relationship between animal numbers and grazing pressure is poorly understood. Any recommended grazing regime will be uncertain and based on estimates.

2.4.2 Lack of Scrub Regeneration

There is currently no natural regeneration of sub-arctic willow scrub at Ben Lawers. A major limiting factor is the lack of seed source because most of the scrub species are not producing seeds. This is believed to be the consequence of heavy browsing over a long period of time which has caused mortality of individuals and inhibited establishment of young plants, resulting in the current low-density population of the willow species. The implications of this low density for reproduction are particularly important for these species because willows are dioecious. For pollination to occur, individuals of the opposite sex must be in close proximity to each other, which at low densities is unlikely.

2.1
Obligations and policies

2.2
Selection & evaluation of the key features

2.3
Objectives, current condition and impacts of grazing on the key features

2.4
Factors affecting the management of the key features

2.5
Rationale and recommendations for grazing management

2.6
Monitoring projects

2.7
Prescriptions

This lack of seed source and low density means that even if current browsing pressure is reduced sufficiently to permit the growth of individuals, regeneration will not occur.

2.4.3 Ownership of Grazing Rights

Tenure is complicated at Ben Lawers. NTS owns a large area of the cSAC and their objectives include nature conservation. However, at present, NTS controls grazing only on the Morenish unit. On the Ben Lawers hill, grazing rights and the control of sheep are mainly in the hands of farmers who wish to maximise economic returns from sheep farming. Grazing rights may be purchased or re-negotiated if farmers are willing, but in the short term, there are no options for change.

2.4.4 *Nardus*-dominated Acid Grassland

The lower slopes of Ben Lawers support a large extent of *Nardus*-dominated acid grassland. This influences the management of grazing in two main ways. Firstly, this vegetation type is of poor forage quality; its nutritional value depends on the proportion within the sward of finer grasses such as *Festuca* spp. and *Agrostis* spp. and although this is variable across the site, it is generally low. As a result, large areas of the lower slopes offer little good quality forage, which encourages sheep to move uphill and to use areas which support Annex I habitats. Secondly, this acid grassland is of low nature conservation value in itself and is believed to have developed as a result of moderately heavy grazing, probably from heath vegetation. Decisions must be made about whether to increase the forage quality of this vegetation to aid sheep management, or to increase its conservation value, for example by restoring heath.

2.5 Rationale and Recommendations for Grazing Management

- *select the ideal grazing pattern for the whole site*

- *discuss how herbivores could be managed to achieve the ideal grazing pattern*

- *consider any constraints on implementing grazing management*

- *make recommendations for the practical management of grazing animals on the site*

Content and Purpose

THE FINAL STAGES FOR DEVELOPING RECOMMENDATIONS FOR GRAZING MANAGEMENT

Select an ideal grazing pattern for the whole site (2.5.1).

⬇

Determine the herbivore management required to achieve the ideal grazing pattern (2.5.2).

⬇

Consider any constraints upon herbivore management and make practical recommendations for grazing management (2.5.3).

This component of the grazing plan incorporates the final stages of making decisions about grazing management for the site. The discussion includes determining how objectives could be achieved with grazing management, the options for managing grazing and the practical problems. This concludes with recommendations for practical herbivore management.

The box 'The Final Stages for Developing Recommendations for Grazing Management' shows the basic stages; the full process is shown in detail in Chart 2.3, (page 56).

2.5.1 Choosing the Ideal Grazing Pattern for the Site

The ideal grazing pattern for the whole site defines the grazing required in terms of the grazing pressure, timing, location and the degree of selectivity. See Information box 2 (page 32) for a definition.

INFORMATION BOX 10: Ideal Grazing Pattern for the Site

Once an ideal grazing pattern for each key feature has been determined, the **ideal grazing pattern for the site** must be selected. This involves comparing the range of ideal patterns for the key features, contrasting them and reaching a compromise where necessary, to conclude with a grazing pattern for the site which will best achieve the objectives. It may not be possible to find one grazing pattern to meet every objective, but the grazing pattern selected should be the best option or compromise for the whole site.

Grazing management will be aimed at meeting objectives for individual key features, but will be implemented at a site or management unit level. So the first step to making decisions about grazing management is to consider the objectives at site level. This involves looking at the objectives for the key features as a group of objectives for the site. Most sites will have more than one key feature and different features may require different grazing patterns.

Conflict of this nature is a factor affecting the management of the key features. This conflict must be resolved to select a range of objectives for the whole site.

The process is outlined in the box 'The Process for Selecting an Ideal Grazing Pattern for the Whole Site' in four steps and further details of each step are given below.

THE PROCESS FOR SELECTING AN IDEAL GRAZING PATTERN FOR THE WHOLE SITE

Summarise the conclusions of the discussion of the impacts of grazing on each key feature.

⬇

Identify any conflicts between features in terms of the ideal grazing pattern required.

⬇

Consider options for resolving the conflicts if necessary.

⬇

Conclude with an ideal grazing pattern for the whole site
and a full list of objectives for the whole site.

1. Summarise the conclusions of the discussions of the impacts of grazing on the individual key features
- aim to identify the main impacts of grazing on each feature; include the ideal grazing regime, grazing patterns which are expected to be damaging and any grazing pattern which, although not optimal, is not expected to cause significant loss or damage to a feature

- note any uncertainties in the impacts of grazing, or any features for which

the ideal grazing pattern is unknown; in these cases, use what is known about the current impacts of grazing to indicate the required direction of change to the grazing regime

- compare the options for changing the grazing regime with the current grazing regime and present this information in a table as shown in Example box 7. The column headings refer to broad categories of grazing pattern and the best option for each feature is shown.

EXAMPLE BOX 7: Table - The Predicted Impacts on Key Features of Broad Categories of Grazing Regime, Compared with Current Regime

Feature	Increased Grazing	Decreased Grazing	No Grazing	Late Summer Grazing Only
1	continue to decline	no change	positive, **best option**	no change
2	unknown; very heavy grazing negative impact	unknown	probably negative	positive, **best option**

---

2. Identify any conflicts between the features in terms of the ideal grazing pattern required for each.
- describe the conflicts; what features require different grazing patterns?

- indicate the extent of conflict; focus on the different grazing patterns required and the options for achieving a compromise: is there one pattern of grazing that favours some features and although not optimal for others, would not be damaging, at least in the short-term?

3. Consider the options for resolving conflicts between the features. At this stage there is a collection of individual feature objectives. If objectives have been prioritised (see Information box

11) in resolving the conflicts then certain objectives may have been rejected in favour of higher priority objectives. Compile a new list of the revised objectives; these are the objectives which the plan aims to meet to the site level. A range of options are described in Information boxes 11 - 14. Think about each option in turn and select the best. During this process, think about the factors affecting the management of the key features, to assess how feasible each option would be. There may be constraints that make certain options impossible and these can be rejected here. Potentially important factors are noted in the information boxes with each option.

2.1
Obligations and policies

2.2
Selection & evaluation of the key features

2.3
Objectives, current condition and impacts of grazing on the key features

2.4
Factors affecting the management of the key features

2.5
Rationale and recommendations for grazing management

2.6
Monitoring projects

2.7
Prescriptions

4. Conclude the discussion with:
- a list of objectives selected for the site, or for each management unit as appropriate if this does not include all of the individual key feature objectives because it was necessary to prioritise objectives to resolve conflicts

- an ideal grazing pattern for the whole site, or for management units, aimed at meeting the objectives. Include details of the required grazing pressure, distribution of grazing, seasonal variations in grazing and the degree of selectivity required.

INFORMATION BOX 11: Option 1 for Resolving Conflicts Between Features

Prioritise the Features
For most plans, it should be possible to prioritise the key features, based on their conservation status. The order of priority is dictated by the decisions made for component 2.1. Allocate the features to categories of similar status and consider whether one grazing pattern could be implemented to meet the objectives for the highest priority features. Is there conflict within the groups of features? If not, decide whether features from the next level of priority can be maintained with the same grazing pattern.

The aim of prioritising features is to find out if there is one grazing regime which will meet the objectives for all of the most important features, but this means that objectives for lower priority features will not be met. This approach will not work if there are conflicts between features of the same status.

If one grazing pattern would meet the highest ranking objectives, discuss the impacts on the remaining key features; would this be acceptable?
With this option, only the objectives for a group of high priority features will be met.

INFORMATION BOX 12: Option 2 for Resolving Conflicts Between Features

Vary the Grazing Regime Spatially on the Site
The option of varying the grazing regime spatially should be considered at different scales.

Key Feature Scale
Discuss the possibility of varying the grazing regime according to the distribution of the key features, with each feature receiving its optimal, or next best, grazing regime. This will require a good knowledge of the distribution of features on the site. This option could be constrained by the distribution of the key features; for example if there are mosaics of key features that require different grazing patterns, this option will not be practical.
This option would attempt to meet all of the feature objectives on the site.

Larger Scale
If grazing cannot be varied at the feature scale, options for varying it at a larger scale should be discussed. For example, it may be possible to vary grazing between management units. It is likely to be more practical to attempt to vary grazing with management unit than with features, because herbivore management may vary at this scale anyway. To determine how practical this option is, consider whether the distribution of the features allows the division of the site into areas which support features that require similar grazing patterns. The herbivore species present could constrain this option; it will be more difficult to control the distribution of wild animals than domestic stock. Consider also how practical it would be to sub-divide the site. Would fences be needed and if so, is this a likely option?
This option would mean that different objectives would be met on different parts of the site. Loss or decline may have to be accepted for some features in some areas. It may be possible to meet all of the objectives over the site as a whole, while accepting loss in some places.

2.5.2 Determining the Stocking Regime to Achieve the Ideal Grazing Pattern

The steps so far described have led to a proposed ideal grazing pattern. The next step is to decide how herbivores should be managed to produce this pattern. To do this, it is necessary to consider:

- how existing or introduced herbivores can be managed positively, to achieve the objectives for the site

- how existing herbivores should be managed to minimise or eliminate any negative impact

The ideal grazing pattern for the site defines what is required from the grazing animals. The present section deals first with the positive management of herbivores to achieve this ideal; controlling damaging impacts of existing herbivores is treated as a factor affecting the management of the key features.

The ideal stocking regime should be defined in terms of a set of characteristics, as listed in the box below. Further details of how to make decisions for each element are given in Information boxes 15 - 22.

DEFINE THE IDEAL STOCKING RATE IN TERMS OF:

herbivore species;
can existing herbivores be used to achieve the grazing pattern?

herbivore breed

herbivore sex

seasonal distribution

spatial distribution

number/density;
consider first the existing herbivores

2.1
Obligations and policies

2.2
Selection & evaluation of the key features

2.3
Objectives, current condition and impacts of grazing on the key features

2.4
Factors affecting the management of the key features

2.5
Rationale and recommendations for grazing management

2.6
Monitoring projects

2.7
Prescriptions

INFORMATION BOX 15: Selecting the Appropriate Herbivore Species

Herbivore species vary in their foraging behaviour and distribution. Consider the foraging behaviour of different species in terms of how selective they are and which vegetation types they are most likely to graze. As far as possible, try to choose the species which best suits the requirements for the site, using either existing herbivores or domestic species which are commonly kept in the area and could be introduced. If wild herbivores are present, the possibilities for using them to achieve the ideal grazing regime should be considered; think about their distribution and foraging behaviour, but not the practicalities of management at this stage. Gather information on the herbivore species within your area to determine the best species for the site and also to predict the impacts of existing species. Specific details of the foraging behaviour of sheep, cattle, red deer and roe deer are given in Appendices 6, 7 and 8.

INFORMATION BOX 16: Selecting the Appropriate Herbivore Breed and Sex

Foraging behaviour and distribution will vary to some extent between different breeds of the same domestic herbivore species and may also vary between sexes. For example, different breeds of sheep will range differently and will often select different forage. Male and female red deer often select different diets, and this can also apply to sheep. Consider these variations to select the most appropriate type of herbivore or to predict the impacts of existing herbivores.

INFORMATION BOX 17: Describing Seasonal and Spatial Elements of the Stocking Regime

The distribution of herbivores across the site will vary with factors such as herbivore species and time of year. Consider existing knowledge about the herbivores present at the site to predict how they will be distributed across the site and overlay this with the spatial and seasonal distribution required in the ideal grazing pattern for the site.

INFORMATION BOX 18: Estimating the Appropriate Number/Density of Herbivores

To make decisions about herbivore density, consider first what density of existing herbivore species would be desirable, before thinking about the options for introducing new species or breeds. Some of the available tools for estimating density are described in Information boxes 19 - 22, but these must be used with care. Their use and some of the limitations of each are discussed. Note that in general, it is possible only to estimate the density of herbivores required and changes should be made cautiously at first, allowing for further change in the future, depending on the results of monitoring.

INFORMATION BOX 19: Sources of Information for Determining Appropriate Herbivore Densities

1. Published Figures For Individual Habitats

For plant communities, as features or habitats for animal species, there may be published figures which indicate the density of herbivores required to maintain the habitat. These figures are based on scientific research, but are not ideal, and although valuable, should be used in association with other information, for the reasons discussed below.

■ This information is a useful starting point, but it will be available for only some vegetation types. As far as possible, use information from similar sites in terms of location, altitude and climate.

■ Research is often limited to a small number of sites and results are not widely applicable, so should be treated as broad estimates.

■ Animals will not be managed at the level of the individual feature and other vegetation present will vary between sites. The utilisation of a plant community will vary depending on the foraging behaviour of herbivores and this will vary between sites, even with the same herbivores. This means that with a standard herbivore density, utilisation, and so grazing impact, will vary between sites. Grazing pressure will correspond most closely with animal density for highly preferred vegetation types because these types will always be grazed. For poorer quality types, grazing pressure will depend on a range of site factors.

■ It will be more difficult to manipulate the densities of wild herbivores than domestic herbivores. Domestic stock densities can be controlled, particularly where there are stock fences around properties or management units. However, the management of wild animals is likely to rely on culling and any counts will be only broad estimates of numbers. Wild animals are often highly mobile and their use of the ground can be very patchy. Predictions of animal densities required to maintain vegetation are likely to be of less value in the management of wild herbivores, except at sites which are quite homogenous in terms of their vegetation.

■ Monitoring will be required to test the effectiveness of grazing prescriptions based on this type of estimate.

INFORMATION BOX 20: Sources of Information for Determining Appropriate Herbivore Densities

2. Computer Models
There are a number of computer models available, or soon to be available, that help decision-making by predicting foraging patterns, utilisation, vegetation productivity and vegetation response to grazing. A brief description of the models available for sites in Britain is given in Appendix 11. These models are tools that may help in the process, but will often rely on many assumptions in order to apply the model to an individual site, so bear in mind any assumptions when interpreting the output.

■ Models include a limited number of vegetation types; many plant communities of the highest conservation value may be excluded. This means that certain plant communities will have to be treated as other types for the purposes of the model and this reduces its accuracy.

■ Models may not include the herbivore species present at your site. This can be accommodated by using 'livestock units' to estimate, for example, the number of sheep equivalents for red deer in terms of their intake of vegetation. Unfortunately, this method does not allow for the often very large differences between species in their distribution and foraging behaviour.

■ To use the models, you will require estimates of the cover of major vegetation types at your site.

INFORMATION BOX 21: Sources of Information for Determining Appropriate Herbivore Densities

3. Current Grazing Regime
A good knowledge of the current grazing regime and the current state of the vegetation is one of the most useful tools for determining what stocking rate would be appropriate. Even basic information can be useful, at least to indicate whether a change to the current regime is needed and in what direction a change should be made. Obviously this method applies only to sites which are currently grazed.

■ Attempt to determine, from an assessment of condition and grazing impacts for each feature, whether a change to the current pattern of grazing is needed and to estimate how drastic the change needs to be; it should be possible to say a 'large' or 'small' reduction in grazing is needed.

■ Use existing knowledge of animal numbers and distribution in addition to the information above to estimate how much of a change in animal numbers is needed, bearing in mind foraging behaviour of the animals currently present (see Appendices 6, 7, 8 for information on a range of species).

■ Avoid recommending very large changes at first; any change should be accompanied by monitoring and should be reversible.

2.1
Obligations and policies

2.2
Selection & evaluation of the key features

2.3
Objectives, current condition and impacts of grazing on the key features

2.4
Factors affecting the management of the key features

2.5
Rationale and recommendations for grazing management

2.6
Monitoring projects

2.7
Prescriptions

The tools discussed in Information boxes 19 - 22 can help to guide decision-making, but none is ideal. There is no instant formula to determine the stocking densities for the ideal grazing pattern. For many features, a lack of scientific knowledge about the impacts of grazing will mean that it is not possible to produce a detailed proposal for an 'ideal' grazing regime anyway. For most sites, the proposals for herbivore densities cannot be accurate. For all of these reasons, monitoring must be seen as an integral part of grazing management which will feed back into the development of grazing prescriptions in the future. Any grazing management proposals must be seen as experimental in the first instance, with careful, targeted monitoring to find out whether the management is working and the key features are being maintained (see 2.6).

2.5.3 Recommendations for Practical Herbivore Management

PROCESS FOR DETERMINING HOW TO ACHIEVE THE IDEAL STOCKING REGIME
Follow this process for each management unit.

Consider the ideal stocking regime.
⬇

Is it possible to achieve the ideal stocking regime?
•
Review the full range of factors affecting the management of the key features.
•
Discuss the factors that are relevant to the management unit in question.
⬇

If it is not possible to achieve the ideal, propose an alternative stocking regime and decide how this could be achieved.

CONCLUDE WITH
Recommendations for practical herbivore management
•
The predicted impacts on any key features for which the objectives are not being met
•
Discuss any uncertainties in terms of impact on key features
•
Discuss possible long-term solutions to any problems that have prevented achievement of the ideal stocking regime

The aim of the present section of the plan is to determine whether it is practically possible to achieve the ideal stocking regime. To do this, work through the discussion described in the box, at the management unit level. Remember that what is possible at one unit may not be possible on another.

CASE STUDY: 2.5 Rationale and Recommendations for Grazing Management

2.5.1 The Ideal Grazing Pattern for the Site

The optimal grazing pattern required varies between the Annex I habitats. Some of the key features require grazing to maintain them in favourable condition, while others require complete protection from grazing to reinstate and/or maintain them in favourable condition. Details of the predicted impacts of broad categories of grazing regime, compared with the present situation, are summarised in Table 2.1.

Table 2.1 Impacts of Changes to Current Grazing Regimes on 'Qualifying' and 'Priority' Annex I Habitats

Habitat	Increased grazing	Decreased grazing	Cessation of grazing	Late summer grazing only
Alpine pioneer formations	possibly negative	unclear, negative with a large reduction in grazing, but there may be benefits from some reduction	negative	unclear, probably negative
Sub-arctic willow scrub	no change to existing remnants in inaccessible places	no change	positive in terms of growth of individuals, little benefit for reinstatement without associated planting; **best option**	no change to current degraded state
Eutrophic tall herbs	no change to remnants on inaccessible ledges, some negative effects in lightly grazed areas	no change to existing remnants and no options for reinstatement elsewhere likely unless large reduction	positive, at least in the short-term; **best option at present**	possibly positive, especially in the long term
Alpine calcareous grassland	CG12: unclear how much of an increase could be tolerated, but flowering of herbs likely to be impeded with more grazing	CG12: positive for flowering of herbs, unclear about longer-term impacts on species composition. Slight decrease probably beneficial, large decrease possible negative implications	CG12: negative	**CG12: positive, best option**
	CG14: no change to existing remnants or chances of spread	CG14: a substantial decrease may be positive and permit spread	CG14: possibility of spread, but uncertain	CG14: potentially positive effect, but uncertain
Species-rich *Nardus* grassland	unknown; very heavy grazing negative	unknown	negative	positive?

The habitats listed in Table 2.1 can be allocated to three main categories; those which require a complete removal of grazing, at least in the short term for restoration (willow scrub, CG14 alpine calcareous grassland and tall herbs), those which would benefit from no grazing during summer and fairly heavy grazing during late summer/autumn (CG12 alpine calcareous and species-rich *Nardus* grasslands) and one habitat which requires some grazing, but it is unclear how much or when (alpine pioneer formations).

The present grazing pressure and timing, if continued, would lead to:
- a complete loss of remnant willow scrub

- some decline of eutrophic tall herbs and CG14, because of the instability of cliffs which support the remaining fragments of these habitats

- in the long term, the alpine pioneer formations (flushes), the CG12 alpine calcareous grassland and the species-rich *Nardus* grassland could decline in condition and extent if grazing impedes

(The Ideal Grazing Pattern for the Site - continued)

flowering every year, but this is uncertain. Occasional flowering would be sufficient to maintain the species-richness, but little is known about the current flowering success and annual variations in this.

Overall, there is evidence to suggest that a change to the current grazing regime would be desirable for all of the qualifying habitats, with the possible exception of the flushes, for which the ideal grazing pattern is unknown.

At the site level, the management of grazing to maintain or achieve favourable condition of the key features is limited by four factors affecting the management of the key features: a lack of knowledge about the density and distribution of herbivores; a lack of knowledge about how herbivore density relates to grazing pressure on the habitats; a lack of knowledge about the relationship between grazing pressure and habitat condition; the conflicting ideal grazing patterns for the qualifying habitats. This final constraint is considered first to define an ideal grazing pattern for the whole site.

i. Prioritise the Features.
The site could be managed specifically to maintain only some of the habitats in favourable condition. These would be the habitats of highest nature conservation value, and some loss of other habitats might have to be accepted.

The features should be ranked to select the habitats to favour. The highest ranking feature is the priority qualifying habitat; the alpine pioneer formations (flushes). It is not clear what the ideal grazing pattern would be for this feature, so there is little information on which to base recommendations for the whole site. In the short-term, the current grazing regime would need to be maintained while more information was collected to decide what would be the optimal grazing pattern for the flushes. This would result in further damage to willow scrub and also possibly to CG14 and eutrophic tall herbs. In the long term, a new grazing regime may need to be implemented to maintain the flushes; this is most likely to be a reduction in grazing, which would be unfavourable for the grassland habitats. In this worst case scenario, only the flushes would be maintained in favourable condition in the long term.

This is a poor option because management would be aimed at meeting the objective for the highest ranking feature only and it is not expected to be beneficial for any of the other qualifying habitats.

ii. Vary the Grazing Regime Spatially at the Site; Patch Scale
The qualifying Annex I habitats are required to be restored where appropriate. Both the willow scrub and eutrophic tall herbs are degraded and therefore should be restored, and clearly it is not possible to combine this with the necessary grazing management of anthropogenic grasslands in the same place. One option for maintaining all habitats in favourable condition would be to vary grazing pressure spatially across the site, completely protecting the willow scrub, CG14 and areas of eutrophic tall herbs from grazing and also ensuring that patches of grassland and flushes were grazed sufficiently. This is a good option because it would aim to meet all of the objectives, but the practicalities need to be carefully considered.

To meet the objectives for each feature, herbivore numbers would need to be varied at the scale of individual patches of habitats. The habitats occur in intimate mosaic, with CG12 alpine calcareous grassland often adjacent to patches of flushes or to cliffs supporting tall herb communities or CG14. This would mean controlling herbivore distribution at a very small scale.

Options for controlling herbivores are described in 2.4 and these will determine what can be achieved on the ground. Herbivores can be controlled by fencing (for sheep and deer), shepherding (for sheep) and culling (for deer) and these methods have varying degrees of success. Given the mosaic of habitats across the site, shepherding and culling would not control animal distribution at the required scale. Fencing options are limited by the topography of the site because most willow scrub and tall herb remnants exist at high altitudes and on crags, where the erection of fences is not practical. Even if fences could

2.1
Obligations
and policies

2.2
Selection & evaluation
of the key features

2.3
Objectives, current
condition and impacts
of grazing on the
key features

2.4
Factors affecting the
management of the
key features

2.5
Rationale and
recommendations for
grazing management

2.6
Monitoring projects

2.7
Prescriptions

(Vary the Grazing Regime Spatially at the Site; Patch Scale - continued)
be erected in some places, maintenance would be difficult and costly because of repeated snow damage at high altitudes. Large exclosures which avoid difficult terrain would not be effective in controlling animal numbers at the patch scale because they would inevitably enclose patches of different habitats.

This option is not practical at Ben Lawers because patches of vegetation which would require very different grazing regimes occur in close proximity to each other and animal distribution cannot be controlled at a fine enough scale.

iii. Vary the Grazing Regime Spatially at the Site; Larger Scale
A second option for varying the grazing regime spatially is to use a larger scale. The grazing regime could be varied across management units, or these could be sub-divided in some way. Decisions about the best way to sub-divide the site must be based on the distribution of habitats across the site, as described in 2.2 of the Ben Lawers grazing plan. This option differs from the previous option because it offers a balance of losses and gains at the site scale; grazing will be managed with the aim of meeting all of the objectives at the site level, but there may be some loss or decline of features on parts of the site where management is aimed at another feature.

The Ben Lawers site is owned by NTS, but can be regarded as two 'management units' due to the different degree of control which NTS has over grazing on its two properties; Ben Lawers hill and Morenish (described in 1.5 of the Ben Lawers grazing plan). On the two units, the distribution of habitats is broadly similar; grazing-sensitive habitats occur mainly on cliffs which are fairly inaccessible to grazing animals and the remaining Annex I habitats are distributed across the site. Particularly large or good examples of a habitat should be given a high priority when deciding upon the appropriate grazing regime for an individual management unit.

The Ben Lawers hill property supports each of the Annex I habitats and remnants of willow scrub. Patches of CG12 alpine calcareous grassland and flush communities are particularly important because of their large extent on this unit. The particularly good examples of CG14 should also be noted. Species-rich *Nardus* grassland is best represented on this unit. Over the whole property, the willow scrub, CG14, flushes, CG12 grassland and species-rich *Nardus* grassland effectively occur in a mosaic, with no obvious geographical separation between the grazing-sensitive habitats and habitats which require grazing. It is therefore not likely to be particularly beneficial to sub-divide this management unit for grazing management.

The Morenish property supports good examples of CG14 and large patches of eutrophic tall herb vegetation which are particularly noteworthy, as are the relatively large patches of one of the main willow scrub species. The eutrophic tall herb vegetation is better represented on this site in comparison to the Ben Lawers hill. However, Morenish also supports good examples of flushes and CG12, the habitats which require grazing. Any sub-divisions of this property would need to occur at a small scale, because, as with Ben Lawers, there is no obvious geographical separation between habitats with different grazing requirements.

The best option for dividing the site will be to divide according to management units and to manage the two units differently, aiming to meet different objectives on each. NTS has complete control of grazing and shooting on Morenish, which means that there are opportunities here to reduce grazing, which do not exist on the Ben Lawers hill property. For this reason, Morenish should be managed to favour the habitats which require very low grazing. The Ben Lawers property should be managed to favour the remaining Annex I habitats.

iv. Vary the Grazing Regime Temporally Over the Site
The option of varying the grazing regime temporally in order to meet the objectives should be considered. This would involve introducing a short-term grazing regime, aimed at allowing the restoration of degraded features, and then changing the regime in the future to maintain all of the habitats. At Ben Lawers, the willow scrub and tall herb communities need to be restored, which would require very low, or no grazing. Restoration of the willow scrub will be a long-term process, involving planting seedlings,

2.1
Obligations
and policies

2.2
Selection & evaluation
of the key features

2.3
Objectives, current
condition and impacts
of grazing on the
key features

2.4
Factors affecting the
management of the
key features

2.5
**Rationale and
recommendations for
grazing management**

2.6
Monitoring projects

2.7
Prescriptions

(Vary the Grazing Regime Temporally Over the Site; - continued)
maturation of planted seedlings to produce seeds, germination of seeds in suitable niches if available, establishment of the regenerated seedlings and maturation of these individuals to produce seeds, at the minimum. It is difficult to predict exactly how long this process would take, but many years would be required. In that time, the low grazing regime is expected to have a negative impact on all habitats which need to be regularly grazed; including the species-rich grassland and probably the flushes.

Defining an ideal grazing pattern for the whole site is limited by the lack of existing information about the relationship between grazing pressure and habitat condition for most of the Annex I habitats (described as a factor affecting the management of the key features in 2.4 of the Ben Lawers grazing plan). As a result, the ideal grazing patterns for each feature have only been broadly defined.

The conflicts between the features are best resolved by varying the grazing regime across the site, between the two NTS management units.

2.5.2 The Ideal Grazing Pattern for Morenish
- Management of this property should favour grazing-sensitive habitats. Priority objectives to be met are those for the following Annex I habitats:
  - sub-arctic willow scrub
  - CG14 alpine calcareous grassland
  - eutrophic tall herbs

- Management should aim to maintain the existing areas of eutrophic tall herbs, which might also provide sources of propagules for reinstatement and spread of the community. To meet this requirement, grazing pressure should be very light on and around the cliffs and ledges, allowing space for the habitat to spread onto areas below the cliffs. In the medium term, grazing pressure would need to be light all year round, but in the long term, if the community spreads to occupy areas other than inaccessible cliffs, it may be possible, and even desirable, to re-introduce grazing, at least in late summer.

- The very good example of CG14 should be maintained, and would be appropriate for expansion. To achieve these aims, grazing pressure should be minimal throughout the year, at least in the short-term.

- Areas with remnant willow scrub should be completely protected from sheep and deer grazing, generally present as small, single-species clumps or scattered individuals. Suitable areas for reinstatement of this habitat by planting should also be protected from grazing. Information on the distribution of these willows and recommended sites for reinstatement is provided in Mardon (1987). These areas are shown on Map X.

- The exclusion of grazing animals will permit the spread of these habitats onto only parts of the site; mainly the areas adjacent to cliffs and areas identified as suitable for willow planting. As far as possible, moderate grazing should be applied on the rest of the site to maintain other habitats.

2.5.3 The Ideal Grazing Pattern for the Ben Lawers Hill Property
- Management on this property should aim to meet the objectives for habitats which require grazing, these are:
  - alpine pioneer formations (flushes)
  - CG12 alpine calcareous grassland
  - species- rich *Nardus* grassland

- The flushes are a priority habitat and grazing management should aim to maintain this as far as possible. Large areas, such as those on this property, should be maintained. In the short term, the present grazing pattern should be maintained, but further information is required to determine what would be the most appropriate grazing pattern for this habitat.

- Patches of species-rich *Nardus* grassland, which mostly occur in association with alpine calcareous grassland, should be maintained. These patches are mainly to the east of the property, close to the cliffs, and to the north of Lochan nan Cat.

2.1
Obligations
and policies

2.2
Selection & evaluation
of the key features

2.3
Objectives, current
condition and impacts
of grazing on the
key features

2.4
Factors affecting the
management of the
key features

2.5
Rationale and
recommendations for
grazing management

2.6
Monitoring projects

2.7
Prescriptions

- Both alpine calcareous grassland and the species-rich *Nardus* grassland would be expected to benefit from summer rest from grazing, with moderately heavy grazing in late summer or autumn. However, these communities, particularly the alpine calcareous grassland, frequently occur in mosaic with the flushes and there is insufficient information to predict accurately what would be the result of a change to the seasonal pattern of grazing on this habitat. Given this uncertainty and the importance of this priority habitat, summer rest is not recommended. A more moderate grazing pressure would be more appropriate, applied throughout the year, but particularly during summer, similar to the current grazing pattern.

- Remnant willow scrub, eutrophic tall herbs and the good patches of CG14; which occur on cliffs and ledges; should be protected from grazing and opportunities for expansion should be created.

2.5.4 The Stocking Regime to Achieve the Ideal Grazing Pattern for the Site

The sheep and red deer at Ben Lawers should be managed as far as possible to achieve the desired grazing pattern on the site, because these herbivores cannot currently be removed and replaced with other species. Sheep will remain on the site for the foreseeable future because of existing grazing rights. The only options for their removal are via negotiation with farmers to either purchase the grazing rights, or via SNH, by persuading farmers to give up sheep and compensating them for lost income. If desirable for the site, these options could be pursued in the future, but in the short-term, it is necessary to consider sheep as a major herbivore to be managed at Ben Lawers, both positively, to achieve objectives, and also to control any negative effects they may have. The red deer are wild and the Ben Lawers cSAC is only a small part of the whole deer range for the population. As a result, the only option for removing deer from Ben Lawers would be to fence the designated area and shoot all deer within the fence. This is not a practical option, given the topography, neither is it desirable in the context of the NTS Deer Management Policy and the Unna Principles (described in 2.1 of the Ben Lawers grazing plan). As with sheep, deer must be managed to achieve the desired grazing pattern.

The ideal grazing pattern has been defined in broad terms, due to a lack of specific information about the relationship between grazing and habitat condition. It is difficult to convert these broad patterns of grazing into specific animal densities, so stocking has to be considered in general terms, by comparing the current situation with the desirable situation and proposing simple changes to the current herbivore numbers.

The Stocking Regime for Morenish

Sheep are currently present due to the movement of animals from other units and estates. To achieve the ideal grazing pattern of very light or no grazing around the cliff areas, sheep should be removed from this part of the unit. There is little information about the deer population and nothing is known about the relative grazing pressure exerted by deer on this area. However, deer are highly selective and will graze herbaceous species and browse woody species quite readily, so their numbers may need to be reduced in the areas where reinstatement of grazing-sensitive habitats is required. Deer are less likely to graze relatively inaccessible ledges than are sheep, and so are less of a threat to existing tall herb and scrub communities at present, although they will limit expansion or restoration of these habitats away from cliffs and ledges. Due to the lack of specific information about the deer, the population should be maintained as it is at present, but as restoration of remnant communities proceeds, the deer population may need to be reduced in the area around the cliffs. The recommendations for animal management are:

- remove sheep and deer from areas around cliffs supporting grazing-sensitive Annex I habitats and areas recommended for reinstatement of willow scrub (Mardon, 1987)

- maintain red deer population more or less at present density on the rest of this property and monitor the distribution and numbers of animals using the area

Removing sheep from this property is not an easy task. Due to the lack of physical boundaries between properties and management units, it is difficult to keep neighbouring sheep off Morenish. Shepherding could be used but would need to be very intensive and would be expensive, requiring either a full-time member of staff, or a

2.1
Obligations
and policies

2.2
Selection & evaluation
of the key features

2.3
Objectives, current
condition and impacts
of grazing on the
key features

2.4
Factors affecting the
management of the
key features

2.5
Rationale and
recommendations for
grazing management

2.6
Monitoring projects

2.7
Prescriptions

contract shepherd, although the latter may not be effective because sheep may need to be moved on demand, rather than at regular intervals. Furthermore, sheep can do relatively serious damage to young woody plants in a short time so it is necessary to ensure that they never gain access to areas of regenerating willow. For these reasons, fencing is likely to be the most suitable method of keeping sheep away from cliffs and reinstatement areas. Options for fencing are discussed below.

Red deer are highly mobile and occupy a range much larger than the property. This means that culling could not reduce animal numbers sufficiently to achieve the required pattern of no grazing around cliffs. Fences will be required to keep deer away from cliffs and areas used for reinstatement.

Options for fencing are limited by topography, altitude and landscape and access concerns. Fences will have to be sited where the threat from snow damage is minimised and on areas with suitable topography. Landscape and access are of secondary importance to nature conservation objectives at this site, but should be considered as far as possible. Fences can be intrusive but this can be minimised by avoiding the use of traditional deer fence; stock height fences with single-strand electric wires set out from the fence on a bracket can be used to deter red deer. This type of fence has been used with some success elsewhere in the Breadalbanes and has been recommended by the Deer Commission (Scotland). It is not effective against high densities of red deer or against roe deer, so shooting will also be required, both outside the fence to control the red deer population, and inside the fence to remove any roe deer if possible. The proposed line for this fence has been developed by the Tarmachan Habitat Restoration and Improvement Project (THRIP) working party which is comprised of NTS and SNH staff. The project proposals are included in Appendix A of the grazing plan.

On the remainder of this property, grazing should be maintained at the current level with the aim of maintaining grassland and flush communities. Sheep densities are low and deer density is unknown. However, the grazing pattern required to maintain the priority habitat is unknown, although some grazing is thought to be beneficial. A change to the current regime should be avoided and monitoring should aim to record the impacts of grazing on the flushes, both inside and outside the Morenish exclosure with the aim of refining knowledge about the best way of managing this habitat. Red deer were culled on the property by its previous owners and this should be continued, at the same level, while information on the deer population is gathered and predictions of their impact can be made. The most effective way of doing this will be to count faecal pellet groups on a series of transects. Details of the proposed scheme are included in Appendix B of the grazing plan.

The Stocking Regime for Ben Lawers

In order to maintain the current grazing regime on this property, no changes should be made to existing animal management practices. The main aim of management on this property, to meet the stated objectives, should be to gather information which can be used to determine the best grazing pattern for the priority habitat, the flushes. To meet this aim, monitoring should be set up as described in 2.6 of the grazing plan, to record habitat condition and impacts of grazing. Herbivore activity must also be recorded.

There is currently no culling of deer but there is also very little information on the deer population which could be used to make decisions about their management in the future. The current lack of information on the deer population means that strictly, it cannot be maintained at its present density and should any changes occur, these will not be recognised and cannot be controlled. For these reasons, information should be gathered on the deer population, to estimate density and distribution of red deer on this site, with annual and seasonal variations included. The most effective way of doing this will be to count faecal pellet groups on a series of transects. Details of the proposed scheme are included in Appendix B of the grazing plan.

Sheep numbers and seasonal variations should be maintained as far as possible. This is constrained by a lack of knowledge about the sheep management practices of the farms which have grazing rights for the property and also by the lack of control over grazing management. Grazing rights held by farms specify the number of sheep permitted on the

(The Stocking Regime for Ben Lawers - continued)
hill land, but unless there is evidence of farmers exceeding these limits, there are few options for influencing sheep management. Estimates of sheep density and distribution should be made, to help to determine the impacts of grazing on flush communities and to contribute to future decisions about appropriate sheep numbers for the site.

2.1
Obligations
and policies

2.2
Selection & evaluation
of the key features

2.3
Objectives, current
condition and impacts
of grazing on the
key features

2.4
Factors affecting the
management of the
key features

**2.5
Rationale and
recommendations for
grazing management**

2.6
Monitoring projects

2.7
Prescriptions

2.6 Monitoring Projects

● *identify the priorities for monitoring projects*

In this component of the grazing plan, monitoring projects are prioritised to select those which must be carried out. If resources are unlimited and all projects can proceed, this component will not be necessary because the total list of monitoring projects will be listed in 2.7 'Prescriptions'.

Monitoring is an essential part of site management. It is required to determine the success of management and to feed back into the process of making decisions in the future. Note that recording condition of the features will not indicate the impact of grazing on them, but the effects of a new grazing regime have to be assessed. Condition is determined by a range of factors, of which grazing is only one, so monitoring this alone will not indicate the impact of grazing management.

A complete monitoring programme would aim to record the following:
- the condition of each feature, using the attributes defined with the objective

- the impact of grazing on each feature, in particular the impact of any change in grazing

Ideally, a monitoring project will be linked to each attribute within each objective for the key features in the grazing plan. In practice, the large number of projects generated by this process may exceed the resources available. In this case, it will be necessary to prioritise projects, targeting monitoring towards recording information of most value in the management of the site.

Monitoring commitments can be reduced in one of two ways:
- prioritise monitoring projects; this is discussed below

- record grazing impacts and indicators of condition in a more subjective way, rather than measuring each attribute; this could be based on assessments by eye of obvious indicators, or in Britain, grazing impacts could be assessed using the methods described by MacDonald *et al.* (1998) and Jerram & Drewitt (1998). Refer to Appendix 10 for a discussion of methods. One of the main aims of monitoring will be met with this simple assessment.

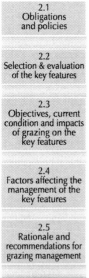

Priorities in Monitoring

In order to prioritise monitoring projects for each management unit, the following aims should be considered:
- Aim to determine whether the objectives for each unit are being met; i.e. whether the features are in favourable condition. If objectives vary between units, it is a priority to monitor the condition and impact of grazing on the features which are favoured on each unit. Other features may be allocated a lower priority.

- If the objectives are the same for each unit, target monitoring at features that are expected to change, either to improve or degrade, with the new grazing regime.

- Aim to monitor the success of any restoration management by measuring the short-term restoration attributes used in the objective.

- Aim to record the condition of features for which there was little information; if the impact of grazing on some features was unknown, these features should be monitored as a priority to ensure that serious damage does not occur.

2.7 Prescriptions

- summarise the recommendations for herbivore management

- list monitoring projects

- list other projects identified in the plan

EXAMPLE BOX 8: Prescriptions for Each Management Unit
# indicates essential monitoring projects, numbers in brackets indicate priority of other monitoring projects

Management Unit	Objective	Grazing Management Prescriptions	Monitoring Projects	Other projects
A	1	reduce sheep by 50%	# monitor grazing impacts and levels for feature 1 monitor condition of feature 1	2.3.1 record sheep distribution in winter
	2	build enclosure in Zone x	monitor condition of feature 2 (1)	
B	2		monitor condition of feature 3 (2)	

In this component of the grazing plan, present a summary of the proposed work; the prescriptions. These will then be developed further to create a work programme which lists specific tasks to be undertaken. The information listed below should be extracted from the grazing plan and summarised here. This can be presented in a table. Identify the following for each individual management unit:

- objectives to be met for that management unit (as identified in 2.5)

- recommendations for grazing management, for example, include the following
  - the species, breed, sex and number of herbivores
  - the location of any fences or dykes
  - the proposed culling regime
  - seasonal variations in herbivore management

- monitoring projects; show the priority of the projects, indicating essential projects and rank the others

- other projects identified in the grazing plan, such as information projects, showing the project number used in the plan

A sample table is shown below in Example box 8.

2.1
Obligations and policies

2.2
Selection & evaluation of the key features

2.3
Objectives, current condition and impacts of grazing on the key features

2.4
Factors affecting the management of the key features

2.5
Rationale and recommendations for grazing management

2.6
Monitoring projects

2.7
Prescriptions

APPENDIX 1

Natural Heritage and Agriculture Designations in Britain

This appendix describes the major natural heritage and agriculture designations in Britain, with greater reference to Scottish designations.

National Statutory Designations
Sites of Special Scientific Interest (SSSIs)

Land already managed for other purposes such as farming, sporting interests, woodland or crofting may be designated a Sites of Special Scientific Interest because of the 'special interest by reason of its flora, fauna, geological and physiographical features'. They are now designated under the Wildlife and Countryside Act 1981. Most SSSIs are privately owned and the underlying assumption has been that the site will be protected by the continuation of the land management practises which were responsible for the development or survival of those features. It is now recognised that positive, pro-active management of the site is often necessary since some practices do result in damage to the features, even if unintentionally.

The main objective for management of a SSSI is the maintenance or enhancement of the features of interest and the SSSI citation held by the owner or occupier describes the features for which the site is important. The country agency provides a list of the 'potentially damaging operations' which if carried out, may impact on those features. The responsibility of the owner or occupier is to take account of the special interests on the site when making decisions about the land-use and to not damage those interests. If the owner wishes to carry out operations which may change or damage the site they are required by Act to notify the country agency. There is a process of negotiation to arrive at a mutually agreed management strategy and further procedures in case of dispute.

In order to assist owners or occupiers, the country agencies are now preparing short management statements which suggest the preferred management direction. Various support mechanisms and demonstration projects are also being developed.

National Nature Reserves (NNRs)

National Nature Reserves are areas of land or freshwater, set aside for nature. The primary objective is the preservation of the flora, fauna, geological and physiographical features of special interest, so the primary land-use is the conservation of nature. A NNR may also provide opportunities for study, scientific research, environmental education and demonstration projects.

NNRs are designated under the National Parks and Access to the Countryside Act 1949 and because of the duty to notify all important sites, NNRs are also now SSSIs. The country agencies are responsible for the establishment and management of NNRs and many are owned or leased by them. The country agencies may also nominate organisations such as the National Trust, the RSPB or The National Trust for Scotland whose main objectives already favour nature conservation, to manage the site. The country agency must secure with these organisations or private owners within NNRs, an appropriate Nature Reserve Agreement or lease which lays down the rights and responsibilities of the parties.

Landscape Designations

National Scenic Areas (Scotland), National Parks, (England and Wales) and Areas of Outstanding Natural Beauty (England and Wales and N. Ireland) are major areas which embrace a diversity of the finest semi-natural and natural landscapes. The legislation for designation varies in each country and the level of prescription varies with designation type.

The main protective provisions are generally set out in development plans or policy notes and are applied through the town and country planning process. Local authorities must consult the country agencies about specific classes of development proposed by the mainly private landowners, so these can be assessed with respect to the landscape character of the area designated.

National Heritage Areas (NHAs)

Provision for designation of NHAs was made for Scotland, under Section 6 of the Natural Heritage (Scotland) Act 1991. They are complementary to SSSIs and NSAs and the designation is designed to operate at a strategic level across large geographical areas where corporate and individual interests need to be integrated with natural heritage interests. Implementation of NHAs is expected to be based on partnership and the voluntary principle. So far, in Scotland no NHAs have been designated.

Local Nature Reserves

Local Nature Reserves are generally small but important wildlife areas and the legislative basis is Section 21 of the Wildlife and Countryside Act. They are designated for nature conservation and amenity and are run by local councils in conjunction with the country agency.

National Non-statutory Designations

Local Authority Designations

Areas of land either near towns or attractive to the public may be designated as Country or Regional Parks. They are defined by and may be owned and managed by local authorities. Participation by other landowners is voluntary. The aim is usually to provide public access and informal recreation. There may be other local designations developed to safeguard particular areas for example coastlines, from inappropriate development and to promote their amenity and education value.

Voluntary Organisation Designations

Organisations such as the RSPB, National Trust, Scottish Wildlife Trust, The National Trust for Scotland and local Wildlife Trusts (England & Wales) may designate areas of land as reserves. There is no statutory basis for reserves, but a number of these may already be SSSIs. The organisations may own the reserve or lease and manage them on behalf of the owner who participates voluntarily. The aims usually are to take account of the wildlife and other important interests and to manage the site sensitively. Provision is often made for public access and education.

Forest Authority Designations

Forest Reserves, Forest Parks and Woodland Parks may be defined by Forest Enterprise for areas of ground that they own or in the latter case, other landowners possess and Forest Enterprise manage. There is no statutory basis and the sites are generally managed for public access, outdoor pursuits and recreation and education.

International Designations

Statutory Designations

There are two major European nature conservation Directives which Britain is implementing. These are the Birds Directive 1979 which designates areas as Special Protection Areas (SPAs) and the Habitats and Species Directive 1992 which designates Special Areas of Conservation (SACs). SACs and SPAs are based on SSSIs and the additional measures under the Directives strengthen the protection of listed wild flora, fauna and habitats on these sites. Appendix 9 describes these Directives and the obligations for owners, occupiers and the country agencies.

Non-statutory Designations

Some international titles such as the Council of Europe Diploma Site, World Heritage Site or Biosphere Reserves are accolades which recognise the quality of a site. These designations are usually applied to sites which already have statutory status such as NNRs, so there are few additional obligations to the owner or occupier other than to maintain the high standard of management in order to retain the accolade.

Other designations arise from international conventions for the protection of the natural environment. These are 'Ramsar sites' (Ramsar Convention 1971) which apply to wetland areas, especially important for waterfowl, and Biogenetic Reserves (Bern Convention 1979). In Britain, the existing national system of statutory sites, particularly SSSI status, is thought to have been sufficiently robust to cover the required obligations and no further provisions have been made. Management responsibilities are covered by those statutory designations.

Agricultural Designations

Environmentally Sensitive Areas is the major designation which covers 785,600 ha of agricultural land. The purpose is to encourage farmers and crofters to adopt environmentally-friendly practises and to this end there is a series of tiered payments. (See Appendix 13). Participation by farmers in the schemes is voluntary.

There are a number of other schemes, such as Tir Cymen in Wales, to enable environmentally sensitive farming practices. These schemes are not necessarily restricted to designated areas of land because the main aim is the conservation and enhancement of wildlife habitats and other features irrespective of place.

Author:
Sarah Eno

APPENDIX 2

Methods of Converting between Vegetation Classification Systems

British systems

Over a dozen different methodologies for the classification of vegetation, habitat or land cover have been used in Britain, partly as a result of historical developments and partly because of the different purposes for which surveys are carried out. This means that sites may have a survey and map of vegetation types or land cover using a classification system which is subsequently inappropriate to fulfil a different requirement. This is certainly the case where sites are designated Special Areas of Conservation because the 'qualifying' habitats are classified according to the CORINE system (see below and Appendix 9) which has not previously been applied in Britain.

Most SSSIs and wildlife sites have been surveyed using either Phase I (a rapid survey method expanded and refined by the Nature Conservancy Council after 1981) or a classification method developed in 1981 by H. Birks and D. Ratcliffe (B & R). This latter method was used especially for upland SSSIs when surveyed by the NCC Upland Survey Team during the 1980's. Many of these sites have subsequently been converted to the equivalent National Vegetation Classification communities, the standard system now used in Britain for the description of vegetation based on floristic affinities. Some sites have been or are being re-surveyed using the NVC. Descriptive vegetation surveys of new sites use Phase 1 and/or NVC.

However, there may be sites where the B & R classification or another land cover classification is the only available map and survey data. Depending on the objective for the site, it may be useful to convert to NVC, especially as this becomes more widely known. Where a site is designated as a Special Area of Conservation it will be necessary to convert the CORINE habitat types to NVC and any other classification, such as B & R to the NVC as well (see below).

The European System

There are a 169 European natural habitat types which require protection, listed in Annex I of the Habitats and Species Directive. The classification is based on a hierarchical system developed by the CORINE[1] biotopes project in Europe, specifically for habitats of European nature conservation interest.

Each SAC in Britain has a Standard Data Form issued by the relevant country agency to the site owner. This lists the 'qualifying' Annex I habitats for which the site has been selected as well as other Annex 1 habitats which 'occur' on the site (see Appendix 9). The data form lists the CORINE habitat and Natura 2000 codes, for example, 'CORINE 54.3, Natura 2000 7240, Alpine pioneer formations of *Caricion bicoloris-atrofuscae*', but not the National Vegetation Classification synonymy used in Britain.

Conversion between Classification Systems

Two-way conversion tables for vegetation, habitat and land classification systems have been published in various forms (see below). For example CORINE to NVC is available in Cox *et al* (1996) but this should be checked with the country agency responsible for the site since one of the major problems with conversions is that the match is approximate, and occasionally communities in one system have no equivalents in another.

The Interpretation Manual of European Habitats - EUR 12 1995/2 contains explanatory descriptions of all the

[1] Co-ordination of Information on the Environment. The European environmental database.

Annex 1 habitats and includes some NVC synonyms where these are available. There is no two-way conversion table from B & R to CORINE. However a B & R to NVC synonymy is published in *Guidelines to the selection of biological Sites of Special Scientific Interest (JNCC 1992)*. The country agencies will be able to provide a copy of this synonymy if required.

Where sites are not classified and mapped under the NVC system, it will be necessary to convert the existing system to NVC and match these to the CORINE classification in order to identify the relevant habitats on the SAC. This can be done using a three-step process.

The example below shows some of the problems of conversions. There are several mire communities (M1, M3) in the NVC which have no B & R equivalent. The B & R equivalent to M18 is not included in the JNCC list but when surveyed, G6 was added. Thus a site may erroneously appear to lack certain NVC communities.

---

1. Convert the CORINE habitats for which the site is designated to National Vegetation Classification using the country agency source

European Union Habitat	National Vegetation Classification
51.1 'Active' Raised Bogs	M1 *Spagnum auriculatum* bog pool community
CORINE 51.1	M3 *Eriophorum angustifolium* bog pool community
Natura Code 7110	M18 *Erica tetralix-Sphagnum papillosum* raised mire
	M20a *Eriophorum vaginatum* spp.-poor subcommunity

2. Convert the National Vegetation Classification to Birks and Ratcliffe (or whatever else) using JNCC synonymy or other two-way tables

National Vegetation Classification	Birks and Ratcliffe
M1 *Sphagnum auriculatum* bog pool community	No equivalent
M3 *Eriophorum angustifolium* bog pool community	
M18 *Erica tetralix-Sphagnum papillosum* raised mire	G6* (see above)
M20a *E. vaginatum* spp.-poor subcommunity	G4f *Eriophorum*-dominated mire

3. Match the three classification systems in one table

European Union Habitat	Birks and Ratcliffe	National Vegetation Classification
51.1 Near Natural Raised Bogs	No equivalent	M1 *Sphagnum auriculatum* bog pool community
CORINE 51.1		M3 *Eriophorum angustifolium* bog pool community
Natura Code 4250	G6*	M18 *Erica tetralix-Sphagnum papillosum* raised mire
	G4f *Eriophorum*-dominated mire	M20a *E. vaginatum* spp.-poor subcommunity

---

This could indicate a requirement to re-survey, especially where certain communities are important for example, where grazing herbivores may have particular impacts.

Conversions may place the same community in a system in several different places in another. For example the NVC flush, M10 appears in two different CORINE categories. A third problem, especially pertinent to grazing plans is the 'lumping' of many NVC communities in CORINE, especially where they require differing forms of management. For example, 'Alpine calcareous grasslands' (CORINE) contains one NVC community maintained by fairly regular grazing and another where grazing should be light or occasional. Therefore, wherever there are problems or uncertainties, refer to the country agency for guidance!

Information Sources:
Countryside Information System. Geographical database software application for 15 UK and 3 European classifications. Available from Institute Terrestrial Ecology, Monkswood.

COX, R., WYATT, T.W., & WYATT, B.K., (1996) *Look-up Tables for comparing key land cover classifications'* includes conversions between nine classification types. SNH Research, Survey and Monitoring Report. Battleby.

JNCC (1992) *Guidelines to the selection of biological Sites of Special Scientific Interest* Publications Branch, JNCC, Monkstone House, City Road, Peterborough PE1 1JY

Interpretation Manual of European Habitats - EUR 12 1995/2. DGXI, European Commission, Directorate General XI, Rue de la Loi, B1049 Brussels.

WYATT, B.K., GREATOREX-DAVIES, N., BUNCE, R.G.H., FULLER, R.M., HILL, M.O., (1993) *Comparisons of Land Cover. A Dictionary of surveys and classifications of land cover and land use.* NERC.

Author:
Sarah Eno

APPENDIX 3

Forms of Land Tenure in Scotland

There are several forms of agricultural occupancy of land, each with different legal status, that are used in Scotland. A brief review of these is outlined below. A major reform of the law relating to agricultural tenancies in England and Wales took place with effect from 1 September 1995, whereby 'agricultural business tenancies' were introduced, but although proposed for Scotland this has not yet been agreed between the Scottish Landowners Federation and the National Farmers Union of Scotland.

Grant of Rights for Agricultural Use of Land by a Landowner.

A landowner who is in legal occupation of his own property is said to have the land 'in hand'. The landowner is therefore in a position to grant rights for use of the land to third parties, by agreements as outlined below. With the land in hand, the landowner can farm or graze the land with his own stock. This will normally create no legally binding rights in favour of third parties, although it is fairly common practice in the case of arable farms to agree terms with agricultural contractors to grow a specified crop (often peas, beans or potatoes) in a specified field for a period of less than a year.

The main forms of agricultural rights that a landowner can grant to a third party are:
- Full agricultural tenancy
- Limited partnerships
- Contract farming
- Share farming
- Seasonal lets

Full Agricultural Tenancy -

This form of lease is governed by the provisions of legislation - currently The Agricultural Holdings (Scotland) Act 1991. The full agricultural tenancy agreement involves the grant of rights to a third party for a period of at least one full year (normally but not necessarily from Whit 28 May or Martinmas 28 November), in return for payment of a rent, and the setting out of rights and liabilities on behalf of both parties. This form of tenancy results in a very long period of security of tenure since it grants full rights of occupation for an agricultural lessee for not just the generation of the grantee, but up to two generations thereafter. Scottish legislation permits the review of the rent payable to the landowner every three years. Normally a second legal document is concluded laying out the rights and responsibilities for upkeep of buildings and fixed equipment.

The change in England and Wales resulting in the 'agricultural business tenancy' - enables more flexible terms, particularly the grant of a fixed period of years for the lease rather than the continuous situation of the full agricultural tenancy in Scotland.

Limited Partnerships

This form of legal agreement is, in effect a means of circumnavigating the security of tenure of a full agricultural lease. Limited partnerships in an agricultural context are therefore a legal device, the main provision of which is to grant agricultural occupation to the General Partner who provides the working capital such as farm stock, crops and machinery, whilst the limited partner (usually the landowner) provides the land and fixed equipment. Nonetheless, a rent is paid by the former to the latter. The main so called advantage of these arrangements are that a fixed period of years is involved - most frequently ten years. Nonetheless they are a legal device, the watertightness of which has been confirmed in the Scottish courts.

Contract Farming

At its simplest contract farming involves one farmer carrying out certain operations for another, entirely on a contract work basis. The contractor is paid a price for the work whether a fixed price or according to a formula such as price per acre per operation. Management of the farm remains with the landowner and no occupation of the farm is permitted to the contractor except to allow the performance of specific tasks. This arrangement applies in practice mainly to arable farms. However, it is also possible to have a Livestock Management Agreement for such agricultural holdings. This would involve the landowner who also owns the livestock in question bringing in a contractor to look after the stock. The agreement would set out the extent of the contractors responsibilities and his rate of payment.

Share Farming

This is similar to contract farming but is more complex in legal terms. It involves two parties contributing to the same enterprise but via their own separate businesses. No agricultural lease is created because the non landowning share farmer does not have exclusive occupation of the land. There is no partnership and the share farming concept does not mean two parties coming together for the purpose of making profits which are then shared, but merely for the purpose of creating crops or stock for market sale. The resultant financial gain is taken by the individual in proportion to his share of the overall business. As an example, the landowner could contribute the land, buildings, fixed equipment, seed, livestock etc; the non landowning business would contribute labour, machinery, seed ,fertilisers, etc.

Seasonal Lets

These apply mainly to grazing use of land and are, strictly speaking and in legal terms, licences to occupy land for a limited period (in practice this must not exceed one year otherwise a full agricultural lease will result). The licence therefore creates the right of a third party to occupy the landowners land - usually for the purpose of grazing his stock but alternatively to cut the grass for hay or silage making - in return for the payment of what is essentially a licence fee, rather than a rent (the latter term applies to full leases).

Servient Rights

This is a comparatively rare situation but one which arises where a landowner purchases property *subject to* existing rights of a third party such as a farmer or grazier. These rights which are normally in perpetuity, will have been granted at some previous date in favour of the third party over the purchasing landowner's property. The only way in which these servient rights can be removed is by negotiation between the servient landowner and the farmer owning the rights. If 'sufficient' (a term not defined by the lawyers) land is also purchased from the farmer concerned, to accompany the purchase of the servient rights, then the rights themselves are not 'extinguished', that is the new owner can themselves continue to use the rights i.e. graze their stock or let to a third party. However if the servient rights are purchased on their own, without land, then by due legal process they are extinguished, i.e. subsumed into the landowners land and could only be reinstated by subsequent application to the Scottish Land Court.

Conclusion

Each arrangement above has advantages and disadvantages for the parties involved, but in virtually every case, for the protection of their interests, the legal documents concerned must be prepared by suitably qualified law agents.

Author:
Sarah Eno

Acknowledgements:
Robin Satow, Factor for The National Trust for Scotland and Fiona Gibb of Anderson Strathern, the Trust law agents for the main text and for helpful comments.

APPENDIX 4

Hill Sheep Farming Systems

The Hill Farm

Hill farms have changed considerably over the last 50 years under the influence of various financial incentives, improved machinery, fertilisers and feeds. The following is a generalised account of hill farming with the exact timing and nature of operations varying in different localities, depending on local conditions and the degree of intensification imposed.

Traditional hill farms usually had little or no fenced land and the greater proportion of hill farmland was rough grazing. Where suitable, some ground would have been used for arable crops. More recently, many hill farms have been able to improve limited areas by the application of fertilisers and/or reseeding. This provides some better quality pasture for the stock at critical times of nutritional demand as well as opportunities to make hay or silage for winter use. Compared with upland and lowland farms however, hill farms are generally low input (fertilisers, labour, capital equipment) and low output (lambs, draft ewes and wool) systems.

Hill sheep land is defined in statute as severely disadvantaged land suitable for the maintenance of hardy breeds of sheep. The vegetation is usually more than 90% 'rough' grazing; that is vegetation which is composed of dwarf shrubs, bog mosses, heath grasses and acid grassland. The productivity of the farm is usually limited by one or more of the following factors; acid, poorly drained soils, steep terrain, high rainfall, low temperatures and high exposure.

Hill farms are still a major source of weaned lambs for finishing on more lowland areas and for breeding ewes

for upland and lowland sheep systems in the rest of the UK. In broad terms, flocks can be categorised according to the level of management, with hill farms the most extensive, lowland being the most intensive and upland more or less between. However, not all hill flocks are managed extensively. Housing of sheep for varying periods may be practised to protect certain classes of flocks from adverse weather conditions and to reduce farm labour requirements.

Traditional hill farms were ones where each shepherd managed his own area and flock (a hirsel) and closely shepherded the sheep according to their needs and the condition of the vegetation. Management of sheep was aided by hefted flocks, that is a subgroup of related ewes which occupy a limited area of the hill where the best grazing and shelter is known and passed from ewe to lamb. Hefted flocks may be less common than formerly when the flock was only replenished from within, there were more wethers in the flock and the sheep were on the hill all year round. These have been replaced in many places by largely free-range and continuously grazed systems, with one person in charge of many more sheep than formerly. Despite the reduction in man-power input, hill farms in the UK are currently dependent on financial subsidies for economic survival.

Hill Sheep

Hardy breeds of hill ewes such as Welsh Mountain, Cheviot, Scottish Blackface, Shetland and Swaledale are able to survive on rough grazings in difficult conditions. Hill flocks are generally pure bred and the only bought in sheep are the replacement rams. However, improvement of hill ground and the use of all terrain vehicles for moving feed has encouraged stocking with cross-bred sheep from Texel and Suffolk sires which increases the value of the carcasses.

The factor most influencing ewe productivity is the adequacy of nutrition although prevention and treatment of disease is also important. Flocks which remain on the hill year round are limited by the productivity of the natural vegetation and the lambing percentage (number of lambs at weaning) which may be about 80% and the lambs small. Where a more intensive farm can provide some improved pasture or supplementary feed, lambing percentages rise and larger lambs are produced.

The ewes remain in the hill flock until they become unfit or reach $5\frac{1}{2}$ years old (four crop) (see Fig.1). They are then sold for breeding in less rigorous parts of the UK. About half the current years ewe-lambs (now known as ewe hoggs) are retained. They are still growing quickly during their first winter so require better feed than non-pregnant ewes, and are not used for breeding. Ewe hoggs may spend their first winter on better parts of the hill or on improved pasture, or they may be in-wintered. In many cases the ewe hoggs are wintered off the hill farm onto lowland areas.

Ewe hoggs are put to the ram (tupped) in their second autumn. They are known as gimmers after their first shearing and until they have lambed. Ram lambs are mostly castrated either at lambing or later, and are known as wethers. Most wethers will not be fat straight off the hill, but will either be sold as store lambs or be fattened on improved pasture or forage crops before sale for slaughter. Some entire males may be retained or sold for breeding, but this tends to be a specialist activity. The usual ratio of rams:ewes that is used for tupping is 1:50.

The major sheep sales take place in the autumn, the precise dates set according to local custom but at this season most draft ewes, wethers, excess ewe hoggs and old rams are sold and new rams are purchased.

The Sheep Calendar

The annual cycle is centred on the production of lambs whilst maintaining a healthy flock. On farms with little or no improved pasture, the ewes spend the entire year on the hill. Where improved pasture is available the breeding stock is brought off the hill in October before tupping. This improves their condition and increases the chances of multiple conceptions. After tupping is completed the ewes are returned to the hill for winter.

The demands on the ewe rise quickly as the lambs grow rapidly during the last six weeks of pregnancy and extra feed, either in the form of improved pasture or supplements or both, must be given to ensure well grown lambs and an adequate milk supply. Where there is enough improved pasture the ewes with twin lambs are kept back and only those with singles return to the hill immediately after lambing. Hay and/or silage is made (or bought in) to provide feed during adverse weather conditions and for routine feeding. There may be sufficient grass available on aftermaths (re-growth after hay or silage cropping) to fatten some lambs for sale ready for slaughter.

Sheep and Conservation

On the most extensive farms the carrying capacity of the hill at the end of winter limits the number of ewes than can be successfully kept there. The use of improved pasture, supple-mentary feed and/or housing of stock in the winter generally permits a greater stocking density than that determined by the productivity of the hill ground alone. The impact on the vegetation, especially dwarf shrubs such as heather, is often greater. Sheep spend more time in the vicinity of feeding stations and, as well as the direct obvious effects of trampling, poaching and nutrient enrichment, the vegetation may be grazed relatively hard.

However, sheep grazing is necessary to maintain many of the current vegetation types found in the hills and they may be used as a tool of conservation management. In order to benefit the conservation of site features (habitats, plant species, invertebrates, birds) the impacts of grazing may be altered by a number of different means.

Such means may be by changing the size of the flock by use of alternative grazing at different times of year; diversification of stock types and the use of alternative breeds of hill sheep

with different grazing preferences and strategies. The distribution of ewes and lambs may be influenced by physical barriers such as fences or dykes; greater shepherding to target grazing; the siting of feeding stations; the provision of improved land; the restoration of deteriorated ground (e.g. bracken infested land); good muirburn practice and the removal of forestry to release more ground for grazing. Any of these options depend on the constraints of the farm and the site characteristics.

Author:
Sarah Eno

Acknowledgements:
Roy A. Harris, John Milne, James Fenton.

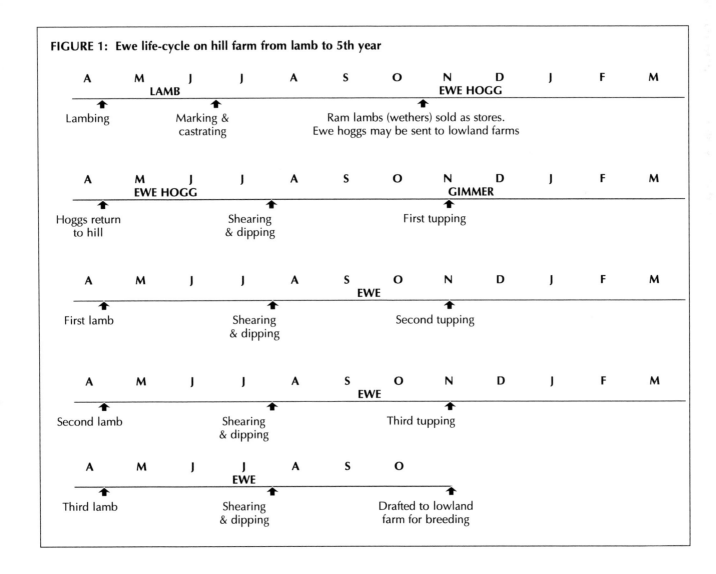

FIGURE 1: Ewe life-cycle on hill farm from lamb to 5th year

APPENDIX 5

Counting Methods for Large Herbivores

Introduction

Counts of large herbivores may be made to estimate population size and/or distribution. Wild species are often counted to help with management aimed at controlling their numbers. The number of domestic animals kept on a site should be known by the farmer/grazier and these species are more likely to be counted to check that any agreed or imposed limits on animal numbers are not being exceeded. Count data can also indicate animal distribution and this information on both wild and domestic species can be used to predict grazing patterns to help with decisions about grazing management.

Two types of counting method are used for large herbivores: direct and indirect, and these are discussed here.

Direct Counts

Direct counts involve counting the animals seen by a number of observers covering a defined area of ground. Direct counting is the most simple method, in that no calibration or calculation of estimates are required, unlike the approach for indirect counts. **Direct counts will indicate only the number of animals present in the area covered by observers at the time of counting.** This point is very important and defines the use of direct counts. Direct counting will only give an accurate estimate of the number of animals in certain circumstances:

- good visibility; if none of the counted area is hidden from the view of the observers, either due to weather conditions or topographical/landscape features

- the area over which the animals range is the same as the area counted

Clearly, this method has limitations and these two factors are discussed in detail below.

Factors limiting the accuracy of direct counts

Visibility is an obvious determinant of accuracy because only animals which are seen will be counted. Anything which prevents animals from being seen by observers carrying out the count will reduce the accuracy of the count. This will be a particular problem at sites with 'concealing habitat', such as dense forestry plantations. If the animals have access to significant areas of concealing habitat, direct counts are not suitable because they will seriously under-estimate the number of animals. Similarly, weather limits visibility and hence the accuracy of the counts, so opportunities for performing counts will depend on weather conditions.

The ranging behaviour of animals affects the accuracy of direct counts because if animals range over an area larger than the area covered during the count, the results of the count will only indicate the number of animals using the defined area at the time of counting. In this context, the count is simply a 'snapshot' in time. For domestic animals, this 'snapshot' count may be a problem even if the whole range is covered because there will be fluctuations in the numbers of animals put on the area by farmers, who may not be willing give details of their stock management. For example, counting could coincide with unusually low numbers of sheep on hill ground during clipping.

In the specific case of red deer in the Scottish highlands, direct counts are often made on individual estates or management units. These counts are made with varying frequencies, such as annually or monthly, depending on the estate. Red deer range widely and the number of deer using a discrete area within the range, such as an estate, will vary seasonally and even daily (see 'Red Deer' appendix 7). A count made on a single day is therefore unlikely to be a good estimate of average deer use of the estate, even within seasons. By chance, counts may coincide with unusually high or low numbers of deer.

To solve this problem, counts would need to be made very frequently which would be labour-intensive. Furthermore, even daily counts will not indicate the number of animals using the area at night which can be a serious problem. For example, in areas which are heavily culled, the disturbance caused by shooting can result in deer moving out during the day and visiting culled areas only at night. Direct counts made during the day would fail to record these deer and would seriously under-estimate the number of deer using the site. In upland areas and over large sites, counting at night using visibility-enhancing equipment is not practical. If such changes in the behaviour of animals is likely to occur as a result of management (culling), then direct counts cannot be used to monitor the effects of management on a population.

The solution would be to cover the whole deer range (if known) in one day, assuming there are no problems with visibility. However, this approach would only indicate the total number of animals in the range and not their distribution between different estates, management units or areas designated for nature conservation.

Counts of whole deer range areas are made by the Deer Commission (Scotland) (DCS) at intervals of several years. Deer ranges have been defined as areas which support discrete populations of deer because there are physical barriers to deer movement between ranges. For each of these areas, there is a Deer Management Group, comprised of the landowners within that deer range. These landowners may count their own deer annually in co-operation with neighbours and return their results to the DCS. This information is confidential, but the counts made by the DCS may be obtained from them.

Indirect Counts
Methods of indirect counting
Indirect estimates of population size are based on counts of 'signs' of the animal in question. These signs include faecal pellets and grazing or browsing damage. Pellet counts are frequently used to estimate population size in a wide range of species. Methods have been developed for calculating population densities from pellet counts, based on estimates of pellet decay rate and defecation rate. The latter has been studied for certain species such as red deer, and can be taken from published estimates. The relationship between grazing or browsing damage and herbivore numbers has not been calibrated in this way and it would only be possible to estimate this relationship at a site specific level because of the many factors which influence the relationship. Measures of grazing or browsing damage should not be used to estimate population size. The remainder of this discussion considers the advantages and disadvantages and the potential uses of pellet counts as an indirect method of estimating population densities.

The Uses of Indirect Counts
The calculation of animal densities from pellet counts requires estimates of defecation rate and pellet decay rate. Both factors will vary between sites, seasons and even the diet of the animals and can therefore only be estimated, with varying degrees of accuracy. Therefore, estimates of population density based on pellet counts are subject to errors. Pellet

counts are generally regarded as better estimates of relative population densities than of absolute densities. This means that the method is valuable when comparing densities between sites or over time, but it may not always give an accurate estimate of animal densities at a given time. Pellet counts are also subject to counting error if more than one herbivore species is present and these produce faecal pellets which look similar. For example, red deer and sheep produce similar pellets, particularly during summer. In these cases, observers must be well trained to recognise the pellets of different species and any potential errors must be considered.

Despite the errors associated with pellet counts, these are good alternatives to direct counts in particular circumstances. A major advantage of pellet counting is that it is a cumulative measure of the animal use of a site. As a result, these indirect counts are not strongly influenced by unusual, short-term fluctuations in animal numbers which could, by chance, be recorded in a direct count. Similarly, pellet counts will record animals which are using the site only at night, unlike direct counts, and hence should be sensitive to any changes in behaviour associated with management. Pellet counts do not depend on visibility, either due to topography or weather, and counts can therefore be made at any time. It would normally be sufficient to make counts of faecal pellets approximately twice a year, depending on decay rate, which means that this method is less labour-intensive than direct counting.

Population Estimates for Management Purposes

Estimates of herbivore numbers may often be made to contribute to the management of the animals. For example, red deer in Scotland are culled on many estates to reduce or maintain population size. Decisions about the number of animals which should be culled must be based on estimates of population size. The two options for making these estimates have been discussed here, but for management purposes, further information may be required. For example, a culling level will be set for red deer hinds and stags, depending on the existing sex ratio of the population, and the desired sex ratio. Pellet counts cannot be used to estimate sex ratio and so may need to be complemented with direct counts. Neither of the two methods described is wholly accurate and when selecting a method for a particular site, consider the circumstances, the purpose of the count and the respective benefits and problems with each method.

Author:
Fiona Stewart

Further Reading and Contacts:
PUTMAN, R. J. (1984) Facts from faeces. *Mammal Review.* **14**, 79-97.

STAINES, B.W. & RATCLIFFE, P.R. (1987) Estimating the abundance of red (*Cervus elaphus L.*) and roe (*Capreolus capreolus L.*) deer and their current status in Great Britain. *Symposium of the Zoological Society of London.* **58**, 131-152.

Deer Commission (Scotland) Knowsley, 82 Fairfield Road Inverness IV3 5LH

APPENDIX 6

The Grazing Behaviour of Large Herbivores in the Uplands

Introduction

Grazing by large herbivores is a major factor determining the structure and species composition of upland ecosystems. The manipulation of grazing regimes by land managers can thus be a powerful tool in the management of upland habitats. To predict the effects of unmanaged, or managed, grazing at a particular site, an understanding is needed of the foraging behaviour, diet selection and intake of the large herbivore species found in the Scottish uplands.

Foraging behaviour

Upland sites are not uniform but consist of a mosaic of vegetation types differing in altitude and aspect. Table 1 lists the most common broad categories of vegetation found in the uplands which are of relevance to the understanding of foraging behaviour of large herbivores. Each of the vegetation categories listed in Table 1 represents a food resource for grazing animals and each has a feeding value which not only differs from that of the other vegetation categories but also varies throughout the year.

TABLE 1: Categories of vegetation commonly found in the uplands, and the altitude and soils with which they are often associated.

Vegetation category	Description	Location
Improved (including fertilised in-bye and reseeded pasture)	Grassland initially dominated by ryegrass (*Lolium perenne*)/clover (*Trifolium repens*) mix if reseeded. Will have been fertilised in the past and may still be fertilised with N,P,K and /or lime. Can be fenced or open to the hill. In wetter areas, rushes (*Juncus* spp.) can invade	Valley bottoms or on lower slopes.
Bent/fescue	Grassland dominated by bents (*Agrostis* spp.) and fescues (*Festuca* spp.). Likely to have a high diversity of herb species if on base rich parent material.	Freely-drained, relatively fertile, soils usually in valley bottoms. Also anywhere the parent material is calcareous and the soils base rich.
Mat-grass	Grassland dominated by mat-grass (*Nardus stricta*) usually growing in tussocks with species-poor bent/fescue growing in between.	Acid soils on hill-sides at moderate altitudes.
Purple moor-grass	Grassland dominated by purple moor-grass (*Molinia caerulea*)	Wet, but not waterlogged, acid soils at moderate altitudes.
Dry heath	Heathland dominated by heather (*Calluna vulgaris*) and other dwarf shrub species such as blaeberry (*Vaccinium myrtillus*). Management by burning leads to patches of heather of different physiological age, termed newly burnt, pioneer, building, mature and degenerate.	Dry, acid soils often with a thin, peat layer at the surface, on hillsides and plateaux at a wide range of altitudes.
Wet heath/ Blanket bog	Heathland dominated by heather and/or cross-leaved heath (*Erica tetralix*) when not heavily grazed but with a lower cover than in dry heath. Purple moor-grass and /or cotton-grass (*Eriophorum* spp.) and/ or deer grass (*Trichophorum cespitosum*) and *Sphagnum* mosses also likely to be abundant.	Wet or waterlogged soils with a peat layer of variable depth.
Woodland/Scrub	Woodland or scrub dominated by birch (*Betula* spp.), Scots pine (*Pinus sylvestris*), oak (*Quercus* spp.), willow (*Salix* spp.), bog myrtle (*Myrica gale*), hazel (*Corylus avellana*), gorse (*Ulex europaeus*) or broom (*Cytisus scoparius*). Ground vegetation can be grassland or dry heathland.	All but the wettest soils, although bog myrtle occurs on wet soils. At any altitude up to the potential tree line.
Bracken	Bracken (*Pteridium aquilinum*) dominant. Where cover is relatively low, bent/fescue usually occurs in between, and below, bracken fronds.	Freely drained relatively fertile soils at low to moderate altitudes.

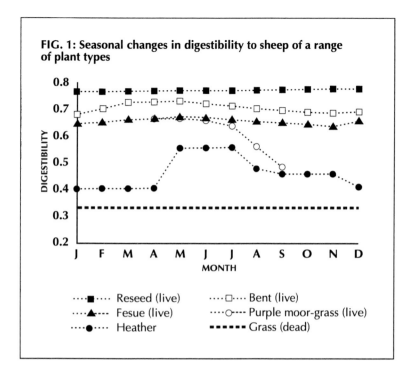

FIG. 1: Seasonal changes in digestibility to sheep of a range of plant types

DIGESTIBILITY

0.8
0.7
0.6
0.5
0.4
0.3
0.2

J F M A M J J A S O N D
MONTH

····■···· Reseed (live)   ····□···· Bent (live)
····▲···· Fesue (live)   ····○···· Purple moor-grass (live)
····●···· Heather   ▬▬▬▬ Grass (dead)

Feeding value of a vegetation type has three components: the nutritional content of the forage, the ease with which this can be extracted by digestion and the ease with which it can be grazed. The attributes of vegetation which affect feeding value include:

- the proportion of live and dead material available to the animal in a bite,

- the digestibility of live and dead plant material,

- the presence of chemicals which are hard to break down in the gut,

- the content of mineral nutrients,

- the size of bite possible,

- the rate at which biting can occur,

- the presence of spines or thorns, and

TABLE 2: Attributes of the most common upland plant types which affect grazing preference. [1]**Although growth occurs in all seasons, most is in summer. This dies off in autumn, resulting in a build-up of dead material unless summer grazing is heavy.**

Plant type	Attributes
Improved grassland	Evergreen[1]. grassland Highly productive and digestible.
Rushes	Evergreen. Low digestibility. Fibrous.
Bent / fescue	Evergreen[1] grassland. When there is a high proportion of green material this is the most digestible of the semi-natural vegetation types. Dead material is of low digestibility and will build up in the sward if grazed lightly or not at all. Species-rich types are of higher digestibility than species-poor types.
Mat-grass	Evergreen[1], narrow-leaved grass high in silicates. This makes mat-grass tough to eat. New growth in spring, which has low silicate levels, can be quite digestible if the new growth can be separated from the previous year's dead material.
Purple moor-grass	Deciduous, broad-leaved grass. Spring growth can be quite digestible but this drops off quickly. The dead material present over winter has negligible nutritional value.
Heather	Dwarf shrub. Only the shoots produced in the most recent growing season are eaten. These are high in tannins, are fibrous and have a low digestibility. Heather shoots have an increased nitrogen content for about the first two years after burning.
Blaeberry	Deciduous dwarf shrub. Leaves fairly digestible when live. Fall off when dead leaving bare, fibrous, stems and evergreen shoots.
Cotton-grass	Evergreen[1] graminoid. New shoots are fairly digestible in spring. Low digestibility thereafter.
Tree and scrub species	Leaves of deciduous species can be quite digestible but this varies with the species. Leaves of conifers have waxy cuticles and are fibrous. Shoots and saplings are fibrous but not usually as high in tannins as are heather shoots.
Bracken	Deciduous fern. Contains cyanide and other chemicals which are toxic to most animals. Any associated bent/fescue can be a very useful food resource especially in spring before the bracken fronds shade out the grass and in autumn when ungrazed grass becomes available as the bracken dies back.

■ the presence of silicates in the vegetation which make it harder to bite through.

Digestibility is the proportion of the dry weight of the plant material which can be converted into energy or animal tissue. Fig. 1 shows the seasonal variation in the digestibility of some of the commonest upland plant species to sheep. Table 2 lists the attributes of the commonest plant types which affect their feeding value. Foraging behaviour is determined not only by the attributes of the vegetation but also by the attributes of the grazing animals. The large herbivores most common in the uplands are sheep, red deer, cattle, goats, hares and rabbits. Horses and ponies are also occasionally found. Table 3 lists the most important differences in the attributes of these species which affect their grazing behaviour.

Range use by large herbivores is determined by a number of factors including feeding value of different vegetation patches, shelter from wind or rain, social behaviour and human disturbance or management. Of these, the first is probably the most important factor. In general, large herbivores spend most time on vegetation types which have the highest feeding value.

In practice, the other factors influencing herbivore movements generally cause them to be distributed over all vegetation types but with a bias towards those which give the highest nutritional return. The differences in the grazing attributes of each large herbivore, (Table 3) together with differences in the other factors determining movement, lead to each using its range in a different way.

TABLE 3: Grazing methods and preferences of large grazing herbivores.

Species	Biting method	Selective ability	Minimum sward height grazed	Particular preferences
Sheep	Biting/shearing. Have lower incisors only.	Highly selective	3 cm	Avoid mat-grass, except in early spring, unless little else available or it is an intimate part of a bent/fescue sward. Avoid rushes (*Juncus* spp.). Eat mosses only when these cannot be avoided. Castrated males (wethers) and Hebridean sheep are reputed to eat rough vegetation more readily than ewes.
Red deer	Biting/shearing. Have lower incisors only.	Selective	4 cm	More liable to eat heather and trees than are sheep.
Cattle	Wrap tongues around vegetation and pull or biting/shearing. Have lower incisors only.	Slightly selective	> 6 cm	More liable to eat rough vegetation such as mat-grass and purple moor-grass than are sheep or red deer.
Goats	Biting/shearing. Have lower incisors only.	Highly selective	> 6 cm	Will eat a very varied diet. Will eat mat-grass and, in spring, rushes.
Horses and ponies	Biting. Have upper and lower incisors	Selective	2 cm	Prefer vegetation with a high digestibility, even if the sward is very short.
Mountain hares	Biting. Have upper and lower incisors.	Very highly selective	3 cm (but rarely graze grass-dominated swards)	Prefer heather on mineral rich soils to that growing on poorer soils. Select grasses from amongst heather when these are available.
Rabbits	Biting. Have upper and lower incisors.	Very highly selective	1 cm	Avoid aromatic, prickly, hairy, fibrous, toxic or low digestibility plant species such as heath bedstraw (*Galium saxatile*), bracken (*Pteridium aquilinum*), nettles (*Urtica dioica*), Yorkshire fog (*Holcus lanatus*) and mosses.

Of all the upland large herbivore species, most is known about the foraging behaviour of sheep. Many of the principles concerned with the impact of feeding value on seasonal foraging preferences are therefore best illustrated with reference to sheep but apply equally well to other herbivore species. Sheep typically group together in flocks of about one hundred animals. The flock stays largely within its home range which is often bounded by topographic features such as streams or mountain ridges. Within the flock, there are sub-groups of ewes frequently made up of related animals. Each of these sub-groups occupies a smaller home range, or heft, typically where they were born and reared. The heft will normally include a range of vegetation types. The individuals which occupy a heft will tend to spread out while foraging. The combined hefts will cover most, or all, of the home range of the flock so the flock will normally be spread out over its whole home range.

Super-imposed on the behaviours described above is a range of others. During the day, sheep will tend to graze on favoured vegetation types, often at the foot of the hill. At night-time they have a tendency to move uphill. This is thought to be an evolutionary response to the threat of predation. In summer, sheep may move uphill to avoid flies, to cool down or to exploit later growth of grasses at higher altitudes. In winter they will use walls or woods to shelter from high winds. Shepherding is rarely carried out these days but, when it is, sheep are normally herded up the hill daily to encourage the sheep to spread their grazing pressure more evenly. Sheep congregate around winter feeding sites, where these are provided.

The need for sheep to find the most rewarding food supply leads to seasonal changes in the grazing pressure on different vegetation types. The graphs shown in Figs. 2a,b have been generated by the Macaulay Land Use Research Institute (MLURI) hill grazing management model (see Appendix 11). This model gives site specific predictions of sheep foraging behaviour and seasonal intake from each vegetation type. Figs. 2a,b show how the amount of each plant type in the diet of a sheep might vary seasonally at a hypothetical site composed of a range of different vegetation types (Table 4). This is just one example which serves to illustrate some general principles and should not be taken as typical since the area of each vegetation type available to the sheep, and the potential growth of each vegetation type, has a major impact on seasonal preferences and therefore on diet composition.

Fig. 2a shows how intake is likely to be distributed between the vegetation types when the stocking rate is low (1 ewe ha⁻¹). In May, both species-rich bent/fescue and reseeded grassland are highly preferred. Although the reseeded grassland has a higher digestibility, there is less of it at the site and it is quickly grazed to a short sward. Some species-poor bent/fescue is also eaten because it has a relatively

TABLE 4: Inputs to the MLURI model needed to generate Figs. 2a,b. Sheep weight is 50 kg. Location is mid- Scotland. [1] Within the dominant vegetation type.

Dominant plant species and average altitude of the vegetation type.		Area (ha)	Ground cover of dominant (%)	Cover of bent/fescue[1] (%)
Heather (400m)	Newly burnt	2	0	5
	Pioneer	10	55	10
	Building	20	85	5
	Mature	10	95	5
	Degenerate	8	75	10
	Blanket Bog	5	75	2
	Suppressed	5	100	0
Reseeded grass (200 m)		2	100	0
Semi-natural grassland (300 m)	Species-rich bent/fescue	8	100	0
	Species-poor bent/fescue	10	100	-
	Mat-grass	10	60	30
	Purple moor-grass	10	60	30
Total		100		

high digestibility. The main growing season for purple moor-grass is later in the year so it is not eaten in May because there is still very little live material. Heather is not eaten because its digestibility is too low. As summer progresses, the new growth of purple moor-grass becomes abundant and the amount in the diet increases until August, when the purple moor-grass starts to die off. Over summer and early winter the proportion of reseeded grass in the diet decreases as the sward becomes progressively shorter. The sheep move first on to the species-rich bent/fescue and then, as this is also used up, on to the species-poor bent/fescue.

By December, the reduced digestibility and standing biomass of the grasses causes the sheep to begin eating heather. The digestibility of the diet is sufficiently low by this time that total intake falls significantly. By January, heather is the second largest component in the diet. In February and March, the proportion of grass in the diet starts to increase again with the limited new growth at this time and as dead material is removed by grazing. In April, species-poor bent/fescue briefly becomes the most preferred vegetation type because, although both it, and the other evergreen grass types, have started their spring growth, the latter are still short after the heavy grazing the previous year.

If the stocking rate is doubled to 2 ewes ha-[1] (Fig. 2b), a similar pattern is seen but the sheep move on to the vegetation types which are less digestible, but have a higher standing biomass, earlier in the year because the heavier grazing rates deplete each vegetation type in turn more quickly.

The percentage of the total annual production of vegetation removed by grazing from each of the vegetation types (the utilisation rate) at both stocking rates is shown in Table 5. There is no direct relationship between

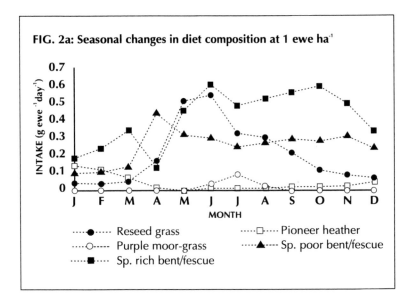

FIG. 2a: Seasonal changes in diet composition at 1 ewe ha-[1]

Legend:
- Reseed grass
- Purple moor-grass
- Sp. rich bent/fescue
- Pioneer heather
- Sp. poor bent/fescue

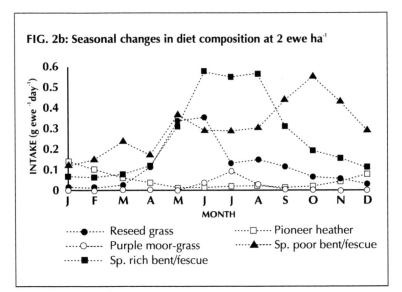

FIG. 2b: Seasonal changes in diet composition at 2 ewe ha-[1]

Legend:
- Reseed grass
- Purple moor-grass
- Sp. rich bent/fescue
- Pioneer heather
- Sp. poor bent/fescue

TABLE 5: Predicted utilisation rates (%) on different vegetation types at two sheep stocking rates.

Vegetation type		Stocking rate (sheep ha-[1])	
		1.0	2.0
Reseeded grassland		88	92
Species-rich bent/fescue		61	83
Species-poor bent/fescue		32	72
Purple moor-grass		4	9
Heather:	Pioneer	16	40
	Building	4	17
	Mature	0.5	3
	Degenerate	0.1	0.5
	Blanket Bog	0.1	0.5
	Suppressed	0	0.1

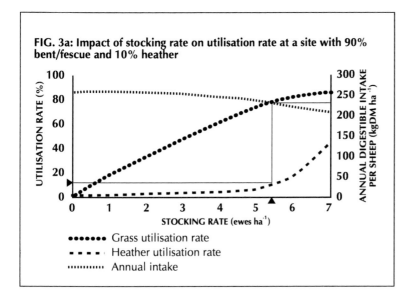

FIG. 3a: Impact of stocking rate on utilisation rate at a site with 90% bent/fescue and 10% heather

······· Grass utilisation rate
- - - - Heather utilisation rate
·········· Annual intake

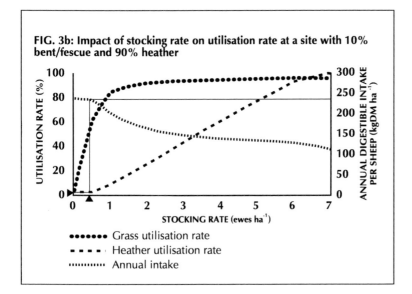

FIG. 3b: Impact of stocking rate on utilisation rate at a site with 10% bent/fescue and 90% heather

······· Grass utilisation rate
- - - - Heather utilisation rate
·········· Annual intake

example described above, total annual intake per ewe of digestible dry matter is predicted by the model to drop from 276 kg to 241 kg when the stocking rate is doubled.

If sheep are kept at the maximum density compatible with ensuring adequate body condition at the end of the winter, without supplementary feed, they will be more likely to graze heather heavily if the area of heather relative to that of good grass is small. This is because the density of sheep which can be supported without supplementary feed is higher if there is a large proportion of good grassland at the site. When the sheep start eating heather, the small area of heather present receives very heavy grazing.

Figs. 3a,b illustrate this point by showing likely utilisation rates (generated by running the MLURI hill grazing management model) of species-rich bent/fescue and of heather as sheep stocking rate increases at two sites with different proportions of grass and heather. The sheep are assumed to weigh 50 kg. The annual intake of digestible material by an average sheep is also shown. As stocking rate increases, the sheep can, at first, eat as much grass as they need, but eventually they are forced to increase their intake of heather as the grass sward becomes very short. At this point the annual intake of digestible material starts to decline. The minimum requirement for a 50 kg sheep to maintain body condition is about 230 kg digestible dry matter per year.

The dotted lines in Figs. 3a,b show the stocking and utilisation rates at which this intake level is achieved. When there is a small proportion of heather relative to grass (Fig. 3a), the utilisation rate on the heather is significantly higher than when the proportion is high (Fig. 3b).

stocking rate and utilisation rate. Differences in the attractiveness of each of the heather types lead to the different utilisation rates shown in Table 5. In general, however, all heather types have a very similar attractiveness compared with other vegetation types. This means that, if there is no pioneer heather, the intake from the other heather types will increase to compensate.

If sheep run out of good quality grass and are forced onto poor vegetation during summer, their body condition will suffer and they will need to be given supplementary feed to enable them to survive the winter. In the

If small amounts of supplementary feed are given, the digestibility of the diet will rise. This will increase the sheep's capacity to consume more forage and it is possible that even more heather will be eaten. However, if sufficient supplementary feed is given to cover most of the nutritional needs of the sheep, less heather will be eaten.

Heather which grows at the edge of an area of preferred grass will be more heavily grazed than that which is in the middle of a large patch. This may be because sheep try out other, easily accessible, vegetation types whilst concentrating on the most preferred. In this way, areas of heather can decline, not because of overall heavy grazing pressure but because of a gradual decline from the edges.

Sheep show strong preference for newly burnt heather over the older age classes (listed in Table 1) for three possible reasons; the relative ease of access to the new shoots of heather, the new growth of grass which comes up alongside the re-sprouting heather and the higher nitrogen content of the heather shoots. Pioneer heather is preferred over the older age classes, probably also because of the relative ease of access. Burning heather in small patches spread throughout the heather areas will help to spread grazing pressure more evenly over the hill.

Heather growing in blanket bog or wet heath tends to be less heavily grazed than that of the pioneer or building phases of dry heath because sheep do not like getting their feet wet! However, if sheep have no other option they will graze both these vegetation types but with a preference for wet heath over blanket bog. Climatically suppressed heather tends to be avoided partly because of the exposed locations in which it is found and possibly also because the current season's shoots are very short and dense and hard to graze in any quantity.

Cattle cannot graze short grassland efficiently but, because of their larger gut size, have a greater ability than sheep or red deer to digest poor quality forage. As a result they are more likely to move onto mat-grass or purple moor-grass in summer. Most breeds of cattle grazed in the hills currently have to be taken off in winter. Hardy breeds can be left on all year but will normally need supplementary feeding in winter. Cattle need to have a water supply and will often concentrate around it on hot days.

Cattle tend to move around their range as a herd. Although they are usually not found on very steep slopes, or above about 600 m, they will move off the more nutritious vegetation and use their range as fully as do sheep if they are on the hill for enough of the year to become familiar with all of it.

Domestic goats are usually confined to lower, enclosed pastures but there are several local populations of feral goats in the Scottish hills. When wet, goats lose heat rapidly. They are therefore restricted to areas with rocky outcrops or caves where they can shelter from rain. Survival of kids is low in Scotland. This, together with the limited availability of shelter, means that most populations are not increasing. Goats, like sheep, live in family groups of females each with its own territory. Males operate singly or in peer groups. The forage preferences of goats are similar to those of red deer but goats have a slightly greater ability to eat low quality forage. Due to their greater agility, they are also able to exploit vegetation on cliff ledges and in boulder fields to a greater extent than can red deer or sheep.

Mountain hares feed largely at night and rest during the day uphill in long heather. They feed mostly in heather-dominated vegetation, preferring stands of younger, pioneer heather. They select strongly for grasses growing amongst the heather, resulting in a diet of less than half heather in summer and almost totally heather in winter when these grasses are largely dead or have been removed by grazing. They are generally found higher up the hill than brown hares which feed largely on grassland.

Rabbits can occur in large numbers anywhere in the uplands (except at high altitudes) where there is abundant good grassland and either scrub cover or sandy soils for burrowing in. They have small mouths, can be very selective and have a distinct preference for short, high quality grasslands. They will eat heather if there is little grass available. The grazing pressure of rabbits is at its highest close to warrens and adjacent to areas of scrub used for cover.

Horses and ponies are found only rarely in the uplands. They tend to graze in mixed sex groups. Unlike ruminants, which have a four-chambered stomach, they have only one stomach. This means that food stays in the digestive tract for less time and digestion is less efficient.

Ruminants also ruminate, or chew the cud, thereby breaking down food into smaller particles which are easier to digest. The process of rumination makes digestion more effective but reduces the time available for feeding. The digestive system of horses and ponies therefore allows them to process food quickly, and in large quantities, but does not extract as much of the nutrients from their food as does that of ruminants. However, with their upper as well as lower incisors (Table 3) they can crop grass swards shorter than can most ruminants. Horses and ponies can therefore consume large amounts of food quickly and can more effectively graze very short swards. As a result, horses and ponies have a greater tendency to concentrate on high quality grasslands than would be expected from their body size. If only poor quality forage is available, they require large quantities.

Interactions between grazing species can be positive or negative. All species compete for the available vegetation. Smaller herbivores, with smaller mouths are able, however, to graze grass swards to a shorter sward height and still gain the daily intake of digestible material that they need. The larger mouth sizes of larger herbivores restrict the efficiency with which they can graze short swards. Large herbivores also have a higher daily intake requirement which they are unable to satisfy from short swards. In theory, larger herbivores will move off grasslands before smaller ones as the grass sward becomes shorter. In that sense, small herbivores can 'outcompete' larger ones. Thus, in theory, stags move off good grasslands before hinds, deer before sheep and sheep before rabbits. Large herbivores are, however, better at digesting rougher vegetation and can survive where vegetation quality is too low to support smaller herbivores. Cattle can graze mat-grass or purple moor-grass to a level which allows more nutritious grass species to increase in abundance, thus increasing the overall livestock productivity of the hill.

Horses and ponies go against this trend in that, despite their large size, they can graze short swards effectively because they have both upper and lower incisors. They are thus able to 'outcompete' cattle, goats, sheep and red deer on good quality grasslands.

Sheep are thought to disturb the feeding of mountain hares. They also compete directly with hares for food and may cause a reduction in hare numbers.

Diet selection
Just as grazing pressure at the landscape level is not uniform, so grazing pressure within a vegetation type is also not uniform. If a vegetation type contains a mix of plant species and a mix of live and dead material, an animal will select the most nutritious diet permitted by the size

and shape of its mouth in relation to the size and distinctness of the different components of the vegetation. Selective ability may also be limited by the amount of time the herbivore is prepared to spend on one bite.

Most herbivores grazing grass vegetation types containing a high proportion of dead material are capable of selecting a diet which contains a lower proportion of dead material than is in the sward. The ability to select live material depends on the size and shape of the herbivore's mouth (Table 3) and on the distribution of live and dead material in the sward. As the proportion of dead material builds up in a sward, an animal's ability to select live material declines and the digestibility of the diet also declines.

At low densities, animals grazing on good grass concentrate on a few patches, thereby creating a mosaic of patches of different sward height. By doing this, they ensure that they always have access to patches where there is no build-up of dead material and digestibility remains high.

Many plant species can have a variety of growth forms depending on environmental conditions and grazing history. Selection, or avoidance, by a herbivore, of a particular plant species can depend on the plant's growth form in a particular patch. Thus sheep generally avoid mat-grass tussocks, but if the mat-grass is growing as small tufts, rather than as tussocks, as part of a heavily grazed bent/fescue sward, they cannot avoid it. The mat-grass is then eaten along with the other components of the sward. If, however, grazing pressure is relaxed and the sward becomes longer, sheep can avoid the mat-grass and tussocks may form. These will then be avoided thereafter. At high grazing pressures, sheep will be forced to graze the inter-tussock vegetation so close to the mat-grass tussocks that they will be forced to eat some of the mat-grass.

Sheep seen grazing on heather-dominated vegetation will often be eating grasses which are growing amongst the heather rather than the heather itself, although some heather will be grazed in passing. If, however, the heather is scattered through a short grass sward and is the same height as the sward, sheep will not be able to avoid it and it will be grazed along with the grass.

Table 6: Live weights and estimated intakes of different species and breeds. Summer diet digestibility is assumed to be 0.7 and winter digestibility 0.5. Add 40% to ewe intake for a following lamb at the start of summer, rising to 66% at the end of summer. Add 45% to cow intake for a following calf up to six months old. [1] The values for horses and ponies are derived using the equation given in the text and the summer digestibility value then multiplying the result by 1.84 to account for differences in their digestive system. They are relatively unaffected by quality so the same value is used in winter.

Animal species and type		Average live weight (kg)	Intake (kg dry matter per day)	
			Summer	Winter
Sheep (ewe):	Shetland	27	0.9	0.5
South Country Cheviot		43	1.2	0.7
	Blackface	50	1.4	0.7
Cattle (cow):	Galloway	455	7.2	3.9
	Aberdeen Angus	485	7.5	4.1
	Highland	495	7.7	4.2
Limousin x Friesian		550	8.3	4.5
Red deer:	hind	80	1.9	1.1
	stag	120	2.6	1.4
Goat:	nanny	40	1.2	0.6
	billy	50	1.4	0.7
Ponies:	Highland	450	13.1[1]	13.1[1]
	Shetland	200	7.2[1]	7.2[1]
Mountain hare		2.8	0.2	0.09
Rabbit		1.5	0.1	0.05

Food Intake

The amount that a herbivore can eat when there is unlimited food available is directly related to the digestibility of the diet and the animal's size. When the digestibility is low, the gut takes longer to digest the food so less can be processed. Large animals have larger guts so can process more food. Intake is linearly related to metabolic live weight (live weight raised to the power of 0.75). The following equation has been derived for sheep:

Intake (kg dry matter per kg of metabolic live weight) = **0.167 x digestibility** (proportion) - 0.044.

As a crude approximation, this equation can be used for other animal species to compare intakes. Table 6 lists average live weights of different herbivore species and breeds and predicted intakes for summer and winter. If approximate animal numbers are known, these intake figures can be used to estimate the likely relative magnitude of the impact of grazing by a range of different herbivore species on a patch of vegetation.

Author:
Helen Armstrong,
SNH Uplands Group.

Acknowledgements:
Comments were kindly provided by Iain Gordon of the Macaulay Land Use Research Institute, Tony Waterhouse of the Scottish Agricultural College and Nigel Smith and Barbara Hogarth of SNH.

Contacts for advice and information:
Helen Armstrong/Angus MacDonald Uplands Group, Advisory Services, Scottish Natural Heritage, 2 Anderson Place, Edinburgh EH6 5NP.
Tel: 0131 447 4784
Fax 0131 446 2405

Further reading:
ARMSTRONG, H.M. (1993). *The MLURI hill grazing model: using a computer to help set stocking rates.* ENACT, 1(4), 7-9

Appendix 11 *Computer-based Decision Support Tools to aid Grazing Management.*

APPENDIX 7

Red Deer

Introduction

Over 300,000 red deer range over more than 40% of the land area of Scotland. As a wildlife resource this population is of ecological, utilitarian and aesthetic importance.

Numbers of red deer in Scotland have doubled over the past 30 years. In some areas, this increase has been associated with crop damage and a deterioration in the quality of natural habitats.

Given this background, red deer are likely to figure prominently in decisions affecting land management. A broad appreciation of the ecology of red deer, in terms of their ecological role, ranging behaviour and options for management, may be helpful in this respect.

Ecological overview

Red deer are native to Scotland and are an integral part of our wildlife heritage. Through their grazing and browsing, red deer can drive vegetation change. For example, where browsing is sufficiently intense, woodland and heather moorland may be converted to open grassland. Red deer can, therefore, profoundly influence vegetation structure and composition, and the nature of associated animal communities. Depending on the objectives of management, these changes may be detrimental or beneficial. Red deer provide a source of food for other animals. Golden eagles, buzzards and ravens all feed on deer carrion, as do foxes, badgers and pine martens. Carrion and dung are also utilised by invertebrates.

Population density

Within the range occupied by red deer in Scotland, which includes both open moorland and woodland, population density is variable, ranging from less than 5 deer/km^2 to more than 30 deer/km^2. At this national scale, higher deer densities are positively correlated with the distribution of well-drained mineralised soils, higher altitudes, low sheep densities and low culling rates.

Ranging behaviour

Seasonal patterns in ranging behaviour are usually conspicuous, being influenced by weather, food availability and the annual rut, during which mating takes place.

In winter, red deer tend to move to lower ground where sheltered feeding and resting areas can be found. Red deer are relatively poorly insulated and lose more heat than black-faced sheep at equivalent temperatures. Shelter-seeking behaviour during this season is common and tends to increase with wind-speed and wind-chill. Topographic features, such as lee slopes are particularly favoured. Shelter, therefore, is probably the most important factor affecting distribution over the whole winter period.

Adult males and females segregate for much of the year. The areas occupied by each sex are often traditional and geographically separate. Hinds in winter tend to occupy areas overlying richer rocks and soils, with proportionately more well-drained grassland. In contrast, adjacent stag populations tend to winter on less fertile ground, often with more heather.

In spring and summer deer tend to move to higher altitudes, following the flush of new spring growth up the mountainsides. Relief from biting insects may also contribute to this seasonal movement, the generally higher wind speeds suppressing insect activity. In times of high summer temperatures these higher altitudes are also likely to provide relief from excessive heat.

In addition to seasonal variations in ranging behaviour, red deer may also undertake diurnal movements. In open habitats deer will usually be found at higher altitudes during the day, descending to lower ground at dusk and returning to higher ground again by dawn. These movements may cover 10km and 750m in altitude.

Hinds are typically hefted to well defined, overlapping home ranges which they seldom leave. Average home-range size varies from c.1km^2 to more than 5km^2. In contrast, stags are less closely hefted to particular areas and tend to live in loose semi-permanent groups. During the rut (September to November) stag groups fragment, with individuals moving to traditional rutting grounds in areas heavily used by hinds.

Feeding behaviour and diet selection

Of all the different factors influencing range-use by red deer, food availability is likely to be one of the more important, particularly during the summer months. Typically, the home range of a red deer herd comprises a mosaic of different vegetation types, the potential feeding value of which will vary both spatially and seasonally.

Red deer are selective feeders, i.e. they exercise a choice between and within the different vegetation types in their range. As a consequence, red deer obtain a large proportion of their diet from a small fraction of their range, much of which is dominated by vegetation of extremely low quality, with high fibre/lignin content and low digestibility.

Red deer, in common with the majority of large herbivores, spend most time on vegetation types which provide them with the highest intake of digestible material. Where the most digestible vegetation type has already

been depleted by grazing, more time will be spent on less digestible, but more abundant vegetation types.

As a consequence, red deer tend to selectively feed on grass-dominated vegetation types, comprising bents *Agrostis* sp. and fescues *Festuca* sp. From a management point of view, it is these areas that are likely to experience the most intensive grazing. Although this preference for bent/fescue grasslands is maintained throughout the year, seasonal declines in grass abundance and digestibility, and the need for shelter, result in an increase in the use of other vegetation types during the autumn and winter. At this time, browse, especially in the form of dwarf-shrubs, predominates in the diet.

While grasses, rushes and sedges, form the bulk of the diet in summer, some species such as purple moor grass *Molinia caerulea*, bog cotton *Eriophorum vaginatum* and deer sedge *Trichophorum cespitosum* are little used, despite their abundance on many deer forests.

The dwarf shrubs which predominate in the winter diet include heathers (mostly *Calluna*), and blaeberry *Vaccinium myrtillus*. Although this seasonal use of dwarf-shrubs occurs throughout Scotland, it is more pronounced in the east, where *Calluna* in particular, is more abundant.

Heather is of particular significance for red deer, providing a source of food at a time when grasses either show little growth or cease growing entirely. In very heavily grazed situations, where preferred grasses have been depleted, *Calluna* may also be browsed during the summer. If sufficiently intense, this browsing may result in the decline and eventual loss of heather cover. Interfaces between grass-dominant and heather dominant vegetation types are particularly vulnerable in this respect. Monitoring of heather cover and structure in the vicinity of these interfaces may provide a useful barometer of grazing pressure.

Tree browse forms a relatively small proportion of the diet of red deer in Scotland. Nevertheless, deer population density, together with the rarity of the resource, can conspire to prevent regeneration of semi-natural woodland. Shoots of both coniferous and deciduous trees can be browsed up to a height of 180cm. Preferred species include rowan *Sorbus aucuparia*, aspen *Populus tremula* and willow *Salix* spp. Deciduous species tend to be more heavily browsed in summer.

The impact of browsing on tree regeneration is likely to depend on a number of inter-related factors, including deer density, tree seedling density, and the availability of alternative food species and their spatial distribution relative to tree seedlings.

Numerous factors influence diet selection in red deer, including : sward characteristics (species composition, digestibility, potential intake); proportion of different vegetation types present and their position relative to one another; exposure; social behaviour and disturbance associated with culling or recreational activities. Disturbance, for example, may force deer to abandon preferred feeding areas for less favourable vegetation types.

The patchiness of plant communities can affect feeding behaviour and diet composition. For example, red deer eat larger amounts of heather, and can digest it more efficiently, when mixed with grasses. Red deer may also select relatively large grass patches within heather moorland. Heather adjacent to these larger patches is likely to be relatively heavily grazed when compared with heather adjacent to smaller grass patches.

Particularly in winter, and in high density populations, differences in food selection by stags and hinds can be significant. Stags tend to feed more on lower quality bulky food such as heather. In contrast, hinds eat a higher proportion of high quality grasses. These differences are probably associated with the larger body size, and hence greater nutritional requirements, of males. Unable to maintain sufficient rates of food intake on the frequently heavily grazed high quality grassland habitats, males appear to sacrifice forage quality for forage quantity, resulting in a coarser, less digestible diet. In female-biased populations, stags may be disadvantaged as a consequence of this competition for food.

Interactions with sheep and cattle

Much of the range occupied by red deer is also grazed by sheep. Both species show a preference for feeding on bent/fescue grasslands, and although deer tend to use higher altitudes and consume a lower proportion of grass, the two species probably compete for high quality food.

Sheep may be the more successful competitor in this respect, and are thought to exclude red deer from preferred grass patches. This may explain why, on some estates, following a reduction in sheep numbers, deer populations increase.

In contrast, cattle may benefit deer, by opening up dense unpalatable purple moor grass and mat-grass (*Nardus* spp.) swards and promoting the growth of heather and more palatable grasses

Management options: culling and live capture

In some situations, red deer population density will be incompatible with the protection of other elements of the natural heritage, or will conflict with agricultural and forestry crop production. In such cases, deer populations will need to be managed.

Culling is the dominant activity associated with the management of red deer in Scotland. Culling can not only stabilise or reduce deer populations, but also provides a sustainable crop of venison and trophy animals for sport. Most culling is undertaken by stalking, involving locating animals on foot and attaining a position from which selected animals can be humanely shot.

In setting culling rates it is important to know how many calves from the preceding breeding season survive to recruit into the adult population each year. This recruitment rate is normally assessed during late winter or spring counts, and is expressed as the number of successfully over-wintering calves per 100 hinds. Recruitment rates for the barren uplands of Scotland average c.33%.

Culling rates are defined as the percentage of the spring population, excluding calves, killed in the subsequent autumn/winter. With average recruitment rates of c.33% over much of Scotland, culling rates of c.16% of the adults are required to achieve population stability, assuming equal adult sex-ratios. In reality, Scottish populations tend to be female biased with c.1.9 females per male. In this situation, culling rates of c.22% are required to maintain stable populations.

The most productive red deer populations are to be found in woodland habitat. Here, recruitment rates may be as high as 55 calves per 100 hinds (i.e.55%) and culling rates of c.27% will be required to maintain stable populations (assuming equal adult sex ratios).

The principal advantage of culling by stalking is the ability to be selective as to which animals are culled, although the degree to which this is important will depend on management objectives. However, stalking is labour intensive and better suited to open-hill situations.

Woodland habitats pose particular problems for deer culling. Dense vegetation inhibits stalking and the typically high population density and productivity of woodland deer demands high culling rates to achieve population stability or reduction. Under these circumstances, shooting from high-seats, strategically located near woodland rides, is more appropriate.

Culling of red deer is constrained by close seasons. Stags and hinds can only be culled during the periods 1st July to 20th October and 21st October to 15th February respectively. Shooting outwith these periods is possible for preventing actual or potential damage to agriculture, forestry or the natural heritage, but except on enclosed ground, requires prior authorisation from the Deer Commission for Scotland. On enclosed ground, unauthorised shooting outwith the close seasons is permitted, providing that certain conditions are fulfilled.

Passive live-capture can be an effective means of reducing deer numbers over a relatively short period of time. The same close-seasons apply, although animals can be captured at other times for the purposes of preventing actual or potential damage to agriculture, forestry or the natural heritage. Except on enclosed ground, these out-of season live-captures require authorisation from the Deer Commission for Scotland.

Passive live capture requires the construction of capture pens within the normal wintering areas, into which deer are enticed over a period by the provision of supplementary feed. Captured animals can either be sold to deer farms or culled on site.

Where captured animals are destined for deer farms, specific handling facilities must be constructed, including race, pens and loading ramp. Provision will also have to be made for acclimatisation to small spaces and for grouping animals for travel, e.g. calves separate from adults and adult stags in hard antler singly in separate compartments. In addition, antlers may have to be removed, and provision made for darting and culling individual animals.

Humane treatment of live-captured deer is essential and a Code of Practice has been jointly prepared by the Deer Commission for Scotland and the Scottish Society for the Prevention of Cruelty to Animals (*in press*).

Management options: fencing

Fencing has been widely used to exclude red deer from sensitive areas, including agricultural and forestry crops, and areas of natural heritage importance such as native woodland. However, fencing may not be an appropriate management tool in all situations.

Fencing is expensive, has a relatively short life and invariably becomes porous to deer. Where woodland regeneration is a key objective, fences may need to be maintained for periods exceeding 20 years.

The normal ranging behaviour of deer can also be adversely affected by fencing. Access to traditional wintering areas may be prevented and, in the absence of compensatory reductions in population density, grazing may be concentrated in vulnerable unfenced areas.

Exclusion of deer by fencing can often result in impressive tree regeneration. However, woodlands regenerated in the absence of large herbivores, such as red deer, may be relatively impoverished in terms of structural and species diversity.

Deer are an integral part of woodland ecosystems and their browsing and trampling may play an important part in woodland dynamics, providing openings for ground flora and perhaps niches for tree seedling establishment.

Deer fencing can be a major source of mortality for woodland grouse such as capercaillie *Tetrao urogallus*, black grouse *Lyrurus tetrix* and other woodland bird species. In one study in Scotland fence collisions accounted for c.30% of adult capercaillie mortality. As a consequence, some estates are now removing deer fencing, culling alone being used to prevent excessive browsing to vulnerable habitats.

Despite these problems, there may be situations where fencing, when integrated with other methods of deer management, will be beneficial for the restoration of vegetation condition, particularly native woodland. Fencing will protect trees until a stage of growth, or tree density, is reached at which they are no longer vulnerable to browsing. Short-term rotational fencing, when used in this way, and when integrated with culling to compensate for reductions in range area, may be an important method by which native woodland regeneration can be achieved in the uplands of Scotland.

Author:
Dr Pete Reynolds,
Capreolus Wildlife Consultancy,
Motacilla, 2 West Point,
Garvald, East Lothian EH41 4LN
Tel/Fax 01620 830398

Contacts for Advice & Information:
Deer Commission for Scotland,
Knowsley, 82 Fairfield Road,
Inverness IV3 5LH

Scottish Natural Heritage,
2 Anderson Place,
Edinburgh EH6 5NP

The British Association for Shooting and Conservation Scottish Centre,
Trochry, by Dunkeld, Perthshire.
PH8 ODY.

Further reading:

Deer (Scotland) Act 1996. HMSO.

The Management of Wild Red Deer in Scotland. R.F. CALLANDER & N.M. MACKENZIE. Rural Forum Scotland. 1991

Red Deer in the Highlands. T.H. CLUTTON-BROCK & S.D. ALBON. BSP Professional Books, 1989.

Ecology of Red Deer : a research review relevant to their management in Scotland. B. MITCHELL, B.W. STAINES & D. WELCH. Natural Environment Research Council, Institute of Terrestrial Ecology. 1977.

The Management of Red Deer in Upland Forests. P.R. RATCLIFFE. (1987) Forestry Commission Bulletin 71. HMSO, London.

Glades for deer control in upland forests. P.R. RATCLIFFE. (1985) Forestry Commission Leaflet 86. HMSO, London.

Red Deer Management in Scotland. P. REYNOLDS & B. STAINES. In : Conservation and the Use of Wildlife Resources, (Ed. by M. Bolton). Chapman & Hall, 1997.

High seats for deer management. J.J. ROWE. (1979). Forestry Commission Leaflet 74. HMSO. London.

Red Deer and the Natural Heritage. Scottish Natural Heritage Policy Paper, Battleby, 1994.

Deer in Scotland. C.B. SHEDDEN. (1994). The British Association for Shooting and Conservation.

Deer Management in Scotland. C.B. SHEDDEN. (1994). The British Association for Shooting and Conservation.

APPENDIX 8

Roe Deer

Roe deer Introduction

The smaller roe deer, like the red, is a native species, and with an estimated population of c.500,000 animals, is the most abundant deer species in Britain. Within Scotland, there may be more roe deer than red, with the population estimated to be c.350,000 animals. Both the range and number of roe deer have increased in the past 30 years. This trend is set to continue as the area of planted woodland increases. As a consequence, roe deer are likely to be a significant factor in future decisions affecting land management. A broad appreciation of the ecology of roe deer, in terms of their ecological role, ranging behaviour and options for management, may be helpful in this respect.

Ecological overview

As a native species, roe deer are an integral part of our wildlife heritage. Through their browsing, roe deer are likely to influence woodland dynamics, both in terms of woodland structure and species composition. Whether these effects are regarded as beneficial or detrimental will depend on specific management objectives. High roe deer densities may prevent woodland regeneration. On the other hand, they may also help to maintain the high floristic and faunal diversity associated with woodland clearings.

Foxes, golden eagles and perhaps wildcats will predate young roe deer, and together with badgers, may also feed on roe deer carrion. At least one species, the nasal bot fly *Cephenomyia stimulator*, is specific to roe deer in Britain.

Habitat and population density

Roe deer are most frequently associated with open woodland, either coniferous, deciduous or mixed.

However, roe deer will also be found in more open habitats, including marshes, moorland and agricultural landscapes, particularly if pockets of trees or scrub are present in the vicinity. On some moorland areas in Scotland, roe deer have been recorded at up to 760 metres above sea-level. Urban populations are also becoming established, with roe deer increasingly being found feeding in urban gardens.

Within plantation woodlands, the age and associated structure of the trees influences the density of roe deer populations. Highest densities ($>25/km^2$) are found in young stands 5 to 15 years old, which provide both cover and food. At c.35 to 40 years old, the woodland canopy closes, with a consequent decline in woodland floor light levels and a loss of ground vegetation. Deprived of both food and cover, roe deer densities typically decrease to c.8/km^2. However, at c.45 to 50 years of age, or following thinning, the woodland canopy opens again, and roe deer densities increase to c.16/km^2 in response to increased food availability and cover on the woodland floor.

Ranging & social behaviour

Unlike the gregarious red deer, roe deer are relatively solitary for much of the year, living alone or in small groups. Larger groups may occur in winter, particularly if feeding in fields. For much of the time however, males and females live separately.

Males are territorial from April to August, the size of the defended area ranging from c.7ha to c.60ha depending upon habitat. Males will sometimes feed outside their territories, and in these situations they may tolerate other males. In winter, territorial behaviour ceases, with males occupying undefended ranges which may be the same as the summer territories.

Female ranges are undefended and may overlap those of adjacent females to a considerable extent. These home ranges are usually slightly smaller in size than male territories, which they may overlap.

Mating occurs from mid-July to the end of August, when males aggressively defend their territories. Females may mate with more than one male, and not necessarily with those whose territories overlap their own home range. Some females may briefly venture outside their normal range to mate with another male a number of territories distant.

Births normally occur between mid-May to mid June, with twins being common. Triplets are not infrequently produced in good quality habitats. Females often return to the same place to give birth in consecutive years.

Mother-young associations tend to break up during April-May, when young from the previous year are evicted. Young females frequently establish home ranges adjacent to, or overlapping, those of their mothers. If unable to find vacant home ranges/territories, both males and females may emigrate, and males in particular may travel considerable distances.

Feeding behaviour and diet selection

Roe deer are primarily browsers, feeding on the shoots of trees and shrubs and non-graminaceous herbs (forbs). In common with many of the smaller deer species, the size of the gut imposes constraints on digestion. In consequence, roe deer are highly selective in their choice of both plant species and plant parts, and tend to feed on the most nutritious species and shoots.

Roe also need to feed more frequently than red deer, hence the affinity for habitat mosaics which provide an intimate juxtaposition of open feeding areas and cover. Roe deer are active day and night, with feeding being distributed in c.9 bouts, the longest of which occur at dawn and dusk. Seasonal variations in diurnal activity are evident, with daytime activity tending to be minimal in October.

Within Scotland, the summer diet of roe deer is dominated by forbs, with sorrels *Rumex* sp. and rose-bay willowherb *Epilobium angustifolium* being especially favoured. Shoots of both coniferous and deciduous trees are also of importance, particularly during bud burst. Roe can browse to a height of c.0.8 meters, and exceptionally to c.1.1 metres.

Woody browse, such as heather *Calluna vulgaris* and blaeberry *Vaccinium myrtillus* dominate the diet in winter. Although grasses are eaten in small amounts throughout the year, they are only consumed in appreciable quantities in early spring, or when preferred foods are not available. Within agricultural areas roe deer will also feed on crops such as oil seed rape and winter wheat.

In the Ukraine and Austria, densities of red and roe deer have been shown to be inversely correlated, suggesting that the two species may compete for food resources. It is not known whether such a relationship exists in Scotland, but if competition does occur here, the intensity is likely to be greatest during the winter months, when both species browse heather.

Management options

Roe deer populations in Scotland are managed for a number of reasons, including the prevention of damage to agricultural and forestry crops, the protection of natural heritage interests (e.g. native woodland), and exploitation as a game species (trophy hunting and venison production). With proposed increases in the area of woodland habitat in Scotland, roe deer populations are likely to continue to expand, with a concomitant increase in the need for population management.

Culling is the dominant activity associated with the management of roe deer in Scotland, with c. 40,000 animals being shot annually. In setting culling rates it is essential to obtain some idea of annual recruitment i.e. a measure of the number of kids from the preceding breeding season surviving to enter the adult population each year. This information is best obtained during the autumn/winter, when the ratio of kids to adult females can be assessed. Spring counts are inappropriate because of the difficulty in distinguishing juvenile roe deer (8 to 10 months of age) from adults.

Recruitment rates, expressed as the number of surviving kids per 100 hinds, vary annually and also between sites in the same year. Most kid mortality probably occurs during the first few weeks of life, and periods of cold wet weather at this time can considerably increase kid mortality rates. The mean recruitment rate assessed at 7 sites in Britain was 49% (range 14% to 84%). Three of these sites were located in Scotland, where the mean recruitment rate was 29% (range 14% to 44%), perhaps reflecting less favourable climatic and feeding conditions. With average recruitment rates of say 29% to 49%, annual culling rates of c.15% to 25% of the adults are likely to be required to maintain stable populations, assuming an equal adult sex ratio. Where adult sex ratios are female-biased, slightly higher culling rates will be required.

Traditionally, culling rates of 30% to 40% were thought to be required to stabilise roe deer populations. However, it is now apparent that these figures were based on underestimates of losses of potential embryos between fertilisation and implantation, and of

weather-induced mortality immediately following calving.

In applying culling rates we need to have some idea of the total number of deer in the population being managed. This can be indirectly assessed by counting dung groups within representative habitats and then computing an estimate of deer density. Alternatively, where the terrain is suitable, estimates of deer density can be obtained from vantage point counts. Both methods are fully described in Forestry Commission Bulletin 105.

Culling is usually undertaken by stalking or by shooting from strategically located high-seats within woodland clearings. Culling is labour intensive, with c.2 days (or part days) being required for each roe deer culled. Culling seasons are prescribed by law, males being shot during the period 1st April to 20th October, and females between 21st October to March 31st. As with red deer, shooting outwith these periods is possible for preventing actual or potential damage to agriculture, forestry or the natural heritage. With the exception of enclosed ground, such out-of-season shooting requires prior authorisation from the Deer Commission for Scotland. On enclosed ground, unauthorised shooting outwith the close seasons is permitted, providing that certain conditions are fulfilled.

Other than culling, there are few alternative management options for roe deer. While fencing may be appropriate in some situations, the disadvantages listed previously with respect to red deer, also pertain. Given that culling is likely to be the principal option for manipulating roe deer populations, much can be done in terms of woodland design and management to facilitate culling. In particular, a network of open areas (glades) within the forest will prove to be attractive for feeding deer and provide an opportunity for humane culling. Two to five glades per km^2 of forest, each 0.1ha to 1ha in area and linked to a network of stalking paths or tracks will considerably improve opportunities for the effective management of roe deer populations.

Author:

Dr Pete Reynolds,
Capreolus Wildlife Consultancy,
Motacilla, 2 West Point, Garvald,
East Lothian EH41 4LN
Tel/Fax 01620 830398

Contacts for Advice & Further Information:
as for Red Deer.

Further reading:

Deer (Scotland) Act 1996 SNH I & A Note No. 4

Roe Deer. J.K. FAWCETT. Mammal Society/British Deer Society joint publication. 1997

Roe Deer Biology and Management. P.R. RATCLIFFE & B.A. MAYLE. (1992) Forestry Commission Bulletin 105. HMSO, London.

Glades for deer control in upland forests. P.R. RATCLIFFE. (1985) Forestry Commission Leaflet 86. HMSO, London.

High seats for deer management. J.J. ROWE. (1979). Forestry Commission Leaflet 74. HMSO. London.

Deer Management in Scotland (1994) C.B. SHEDDEN. The British Association for Shooting and Conservation

Deer in Scotland. C.B. Shedden. (1994). The British Association for Shooting and Conservation.

APPENDIX 9

Natura 2000 Sites

Natura 2000 sites are a network of areas across the European Community, selected for the purpose of conserving natural habitats and species of plants and animals which are rare, endangered or vulnerable in the European Community.

Natura 2000 sites include 'Special Areas of Conservation' (SACs), designated under the 'Council Directive 92/43/EEC on the conservation of natural habitats and of wild fauna and flora' (The Habitats Directive) and 'Special Protection Areas' (SPAs), designated under the1979 EC Wild Birds Directive (the Birds Directive). Sites may be either marine or terrestrial and one site may be designated as both SPA and SAC.

The Directives impose responsibilities and powers upon the Member states and were brought into GB law by the 'Conservation (Natural Habitats & c.) Regulations 1994';

The Habitats Directive
The Directive lists habitats and plant and animal species which are important in the European Community because they are rare, endangered or vulnerable. These lists are included in the Directive in Annexes, and species or habitats will often be referred to according to the Annex in which they are listed. Habitats are listed in Annex I using the European CORINE classification system (see **Appendix 2**). There are 169 of these habitats, of which 82 occur in the UK. Species are listed in three annexes which include responsibilities for:

■ site designation, for species in Annex II

■ strict protection of all populations of species in Annex IV

■ managed exploitation of species in Annex IV

There are 623 Annex II species, of which 51 occur in the UK, although only 39 of these have been recommended to the government for protection because the remainder are either extinct, not viable, introduced or vagrants.

The Directive also includes 'priority' habitats and species (see 'Terminology' below), indicated in the lists with asterisks. There are 22 priority habitats in the UK, but only one priority species.

Obligations for Member States
The Directive imposes on Member states, certain obligations for the protection of habitats and species and the management of sites which support them. The aim of the Directive to establish a network of European sites is to be achieved in several stages, following the timetable shown below.

■ **June 1995**
Member states submit a national list of possible Special Areas for Conservation.

■ **June 1995 - June 1998**
Member states and European Commission agree which sites should be adopted as 'Sites of Community Importance'.

■ **June 2004**
Completed designation of the 'Sites of Community Importance' as Special Areas of Conservation.

Sites designated in this way must be managed according to the guidelines in the Directive. The Directive is divided into Articles and 'Site Protection Obligations' are detailed in Article 6. Member states are required to avoid deterioration of the habitats and species, as well as disturbance to species, and to maintain or restore habitats and species at *favourable conservation status* (see 'Terminology' below). Any plan or project which may have a significant effect on a European site and which is not directly connected with or necessary to the management of that site must undergo an appropriate assessment (Article 6(3)). The assessment required depends on the site in question and will be guided by country agencies. Plans or projects which may adversely affect site integrity may proceed only under certain circumstances:

- there are no alternative solutions

- there are imperative reasons of overriding public interest, including social or economic interest for sites which do not host a priority habitat or species

- for sites which do host priority habitats or species, the only consid-erations which may be taken into account are those relating to human health or public safety, or to beneficial consequences of primary importance to the environment or, other reasons of overriding public interest, subject to agreement from the Commission.

Selection of SACs in GB

A list of sites which may qualify for designation as SACs ('possible' SACs) in the UK was published by the Joint Nature Conservation Committee (JNCC). This list is likely to be amended before a final 'national list' is submitted to the European Commission. These possible SACs provide areas where habitats and species listed in the Directive will be protected. The sites were selected either because they support the best examples of the habitats and species in Britain, or because they are partic-ularly important sites which feature several different listed habitats and species.

For each site, a standard data form was produced. This lists the Annex I habitats and Annex II species which are particularly well represented at the site and provides some information about their extent in a UK context. These habitats and species are the

reasons for the selection of the site and are often referred to as the 'qualifying' interests (see 'Terminology'). The site may support additional Annexed habitats or species, listed as 'additional' habitats or species, and are often referred to as 'occurring' or 'hosted' interests. Responsibility for maintaining qualifying interests may be regarded as a priority for site management.

Terminology

Priority habitats and species are those which are particularly threatened in global terms and of which a significant proportion of their natural range occurs within the European Community.

Favourable Conservation Status
The Directive requires that listed habitats and species are maintained or restored in favourable conservation status, as defined in Article 1 of the Directive.

For habitats, conservation status will be taken as favourable when:
- its natural range and areas it covers within that range are stable or increasing and

- the species structure and functions which are necessary for its long-term maintenance exist and are likely to continue to exist for the foreseeable future, and

- the conservation status of its typical species is favourable

The conservation status of species will be taken as favourable when:
- population dynamics data suggest that the species is maintaining itself on a long-term basis as a viable component of its natural habitats, and

- the natural range of the species is neither being reduced nor is likely to be reduced for the foreseeable future, and

- there is, and will probably continue to be, a sufficiently large habitat to maintain its populations on a long-term basis.

Qualifying Interests
Habitats or species listed in the Directive which are particularly well represented at a site proposed for designation as SAC. These interests are cited as the reasons for selecting the site.

Occurring or Hosted Interests
Habitats or species listed in the Directive which occur at a site proposed for designation as SAC. These interests are not cited as reasons for selecting the site and will be listed by JNCC on standard site data forms as 'additional' habitats or species which occur at the site.

The Birds Directive
The Birds Directive provides for the protection, management and control of all species of naturally occurring wild birds in the European Territory of Member States. The protection under this Directive applies to birds, their eggs, nests and habitats. The Directive requires that member states take action to ensure the maintenance of habitats of all naturally occurring bird species within their territories, so that populations are supported at ecologically sound levels. Member states are also required to take special action to protect the habitat of certain particularly rare species and of migratory species. These species are listed in Annex I of the Directive.

Author:
Fiona Stewart

References and Further Reading:
The Scottish Office, Environment No. *Nature Conservation: Implementation in Scotland of EC Directives on the Conservation of Natural Habitats and of Wild Flora and Fauna, and the Conservation of Wild Birds: The Conservation (Natural Habitats & c.) Regulations 1994*. Circular no. 6/1995 Describes the implementation of the Directives in Scotland.

Scottish Natural Heritage 'Natura 2000; A Guide to the 1992 Habitats Directive in Scotland's Terrestrial Environment. Contact SNH Publications, Battleby Centre, Redgorton, Perth, PH1 3EW.

HOPKINS, J.J. (1995). *The Habitats Directive - Selecting the UK Sites.* British Wildlife, 6(5); 297-306.

The Department of the Environment (1995). *The Habitats Directive; How it Will Apply in Great Britain.*

APPENDIX 10

Assessing the Condition of Upland Vegetation and Habitats

Introduction

Assessments of vegetation or habitat condition may be carried out for a number of different purposes, depending on the objective of the survey. It is important to be clear about this at the outset so that the right information is collected. For example, assessments may be purely descriptive of the recent changes or impacts of land management practices on vegetation or habitats. Such assessments do not say whether the condition of the habitat is 'good' or 'bad'. But assessments may also be evaluative, in which case the survey information will be used to decide whether the condition of the vegetation is 'good' or 'bad' when compared to a set of criteria which defines the desirable condition.

English Nature (EN) and Scottish Natural Heritage (SNH) have each produced guidance manuals for carrying out habitat or vegetation assessments for the upland types which are represented within their region. The Countryside Council for Wales has not produced a manual but expects for the time being, to draw on those of EN and SNH. These manuals are:

Assessing Vegetation Condition in the English Uplands. Jerram, R. & Drewitt, A. 1998 English Nature Research Reports No. 264. Peterborough

A Guide to Upland Habitats: Surveying Land Management Impacts. MacDonald, A., *et al.*1998. Scottish Natural Heritage. Battleby, Perth.

Methods of Assessment

Both the EN and SNH manuals present methods based on field surveying and recording of impacts on recognisable units or grid squares of vegetation within a site or management unit. The surveys aim to be repeatable and to be carried out fairly rapidly but there is always a compromise between speed and precision or objectivity. Both country agencies expect surveyors to have some knowledge of upland ecology and to have had some training in the methodology used.

As illustrated by the titles of the manuals, the two methodologies differ somewhat in their emphasis and approach. For each upland habitat, English Nature has defined the criteria which describe favourable condition and grades of unfavourable condition. Assessment can therefore lead to an evaluation of the status of the vegetation.

The SNH method is descriptive of the nature and intensity of the range of impacts that occur on Scottish upland habitats. An evaluation of the condition in relation to the objective for the habitat, such as whether it is in favourable condition, is a later step and is not included at this stage. This has certain benefits in that the same impact survey can be used to inform different objectives or, if objectives change, the impact survey does not necessarily need to be repeated.

Both methods provide a very useful picture of the impacts on the different vegetation or habitat types. They can lead, possibly through additional steps, to an evaluation of the condition and suggest whether or not a change in management is required.

The EN method lists a selection of criteria which best exemplify favourable and grades of unfavourable condition for each vegetation type. Criteria for favourable condition of wet dwarf shrub heath for example, include 'sward composed of a variety of higher plants and bryophytes. Dwarf shrubs should not dominate the sward and there should be a minimum of 25% cover of species other than dwarf shrubs'; 'alien trees and shrubs (e.g. *Rhododendron*, *Picea*, *Larix*, *Pinus* etc.) no more than rare (<5 individuals in any given 25ha)'. Grades of unfavourable condition are also defined. Additionally, for each habitat a range of indicators which illustrate acceptable management practices are described. For example, wet heath should be lightly grazed and one indicator of this is: '<33% long shoots of *Calluna vulgaris* or *Vaccinium myrtillus* showing signs of being grazed where average shoot length is >4cm'.

The SNH method uses a range indicators based on directly observable effects of current impacts. The principal types of impacts which occur in the Scottish uplands are grazing and browsing, burning and draining, but additional indicators such as impacts of agricultural improvement or peat cutting for example, are given where appropriate.

The indicators include ones which are sensitive to the intensity of the impacts, so that high, moderate or low classes of impact can be distinguished. This is designed to roughly equally divide the range of variation in impact likely to be found in the Scottish uplands. For example, a grassland which has a smooth structure, where more than 75% of the leaves are grazed, which has a high cover of bryophytes and shows widespread evidence of bare ground due to hoof-marks...all add up to a grassland which is subject to high grazing. A moderate grazing impact is indicated by 25-75% of leaves grazed, and where bryophytes constitute up to 50% cover etc. What level of grazing impact is 'good' or 'bad' depends on the objective for that grassland.

Both the EN and SNH methods require similar preliminary tasks to be carried out. Before a habitat condition assessment is done, an initial site visit is usually necessary to ascertain the nature and extent of the site, the types of habitats present, time needed for the survey, health and safety aspects etc. Additionally, it is important to take into account the objectives for the site or management unit. Sampling methods and routes, mapping method, what spatial scale to work at, post-fieldwork data processing methods and the required form of the outputs also have to be decided prior to a full survey.

On-site methods require a visual examination of the habitat by walking through a certain unit area, possibly in a proscribed pattern, combined with consultation of the appropriate field criteria and indicators. Recording of the impacts or habitat condition may be carried out on maps as well as on appropriate record cards. In addition to maps it is important that a record is kept of what assessments are made and why. These can be pre-printed cards which record the grid reference, the date and list the criteria and indicators with check boxes that can be easily filled. Photographic documentation is also valuable and is a useful aid to interpretation of reports by third parties.

Habitat Assessments and Favourable Condition

As explained above, habitat or vegetation assessments may not result in a report about whether the features are in favourable condition. Ultimately, this is the responsibility of the country agencies and they will be able to give guidance on monitoring, assessment and management to site owners and managers.

In 1995 the Joint Nature Conservation Committee (JNCC) and the country agencies started work on developing a set of generic guidelines for defining favourable condition for a range of habitats and species. This work will continue through a series of interagency workshops in order to finalise these guidelines and to contribute towards a set of common standards for monitoring designated sites. In terms of statutory duties for Sites of Special Scientific Interest, Special Areas of Conservation and Special Protection Areas, the country agencies are aiming to institute a 6 year programme of site condition assessment and monitoring commencing with a pilot project in 1998, and using the generic guidelines as these become available. For further information contact the relevant country agencies.

Author:
Sarah Eno.

Acknowledgements:
Angus MacDonald, Phil Shaw and Joanne Backshall.

APPENDIX 11

Computer-based Decision Support Tools to aid Grazing Management

Hill Grazing Management Model

At present there is one decision-support tool, entitled the **Hill Grazing Management Model**, which is available to assist decision-making about the impact of large herbivores on hill vegetation. It was developed by the Macaulay Land Use Research Institute (MLURI) with funding from the Scottish Office Agriculture, Environment and Fisheries Department, Scottish Natural Heritage and English Nature. From simple sets of information it predicts the utilisation by sheep of the most commonly found vegetation types on hill grazing in the UK.

The information required is (a) the area of each of the major vegetation types, heather (newly burnt, pioneer, building, mature, degenerate, blanket bog and suppressed), *Agrostis/ Festuca, Nardus, Molinia* (burnt and unburnt) and *Festuca/Agrostis* (and its cover within the other vegetation types, if any), (b) the ground cover of each of these types (if known), the location of the site and its altitude, (c) the area of any reseeded pasture found within the hill area, its soil type, the amount of nitrogen fertiliser applied and its management, and (d) the liveweight of the breeding ewe and the number of ewes on the hill area in each month of the year. From this information the seasonal productivity of each vegetation type is estimated and the distribution of the ewes across the vegetation types is predicted. The offtake by ewes of each vegetation type on a daily basis is then calculated over the period of a year. This allows the prediction of the utilisation rate of the different heather types and the height of the herbage of the grassland types to be estimated on a daily or annual basis.

The user has then to interpret the information provided to judge whether the stocking rate of sheep will influence the productivity of the vegetation or lead to change in the areas of the vegetation types. The Hill Grazing management Model has been widely used by those with some ecological training, to set stocking rates of sheep to meet animal production or conservation objectives and appears robust, particularly when applied to hill areas containing significant proportions of dry heath and *Agrostis/Festuca*.

Windows 95 and Windows 3.1 versions can be obtained from Ms A. Malcolm, Macaulay Research and Consultancy Services Ltd., Craigiebuckler, Aberdeen at a cost of £30.

Hilldeer

A new decision support tool, **HILLDEER**, (February 1998) has been developed by the MLURI and Biomathematics and Statistics for Scotland for use by the Deer Commission for Scotland and Deer Management Groups in Scotland. It predicts from a simple number of inputs, the impact over any number of years of grazing by red deer, and sheep, on the productivity and dynamics of a small number of vegetation types.

The inputs required are (a) the areas of dry heath, wet heath, blanket bog, *Agrostis/Festuca, Nardus* and *Molinia*, (b) an estimate of the biomass of each of the vegetation types at the start of the simulation, (c) the location of the hill area, (d) the numbers of stags and hinds and their larder weights, (e) the culling policy used and (f) the numbers and breed of ewe grazing in each month on the area. **HILLDEER** predicts the long-term population dynamics of red deer and the changes in the areas of the different vegetation types.

Hillplan

A further decision support tool, **HILLPLAN**, is being developed by the MLURI and will be (December 1998). **HILLPLAN** simulates the grazing by sheep and cattle of hill areas and upland pastures including enclosed permanent pasture. It predicts the impact of grazing on changes in a similar range of hill vegetation types to that of the Hill Grazing Management Model as well as changes in the vegetation within permanent pastures. It also predicts the effect of the management system and stocking rate on the productivity of sheep flocks and cattle herds.

It requires the same types of inputs as that of the Hill Grazing management Model and **HILLDEER** but also requires information on the movement of animals between fields and/or hill areas and more information on flock and herd management decisions. The models contained within **HILLPLAN** contain up-to-date data and concepts and should have greater predictive ability in simulating the effects of changes in management on vegetation and on annual productivity at a farm or estate unit level than previous decision support tools.

Author:

J. Milne (MLURI).

More details for all computer based tools can be obtained from Dr J. A. Milne, Macaulay Land Use Research Institute, Craigiebuckler, Aberdeen AB15 8QH - Tel. 01224 318611; Fax. 01224 311556; e-mail: j.milne@mluri.sari.ac.uk.

APPENDIX 12

The Impacts of Grazing on Upland Vegetation by Large Herbivores

Introduction

Sheep and red deer are currently the most widespread and significant contributors to grazing and browsing impacts in the Scottish uplands. Cattle, ponies and horses, roe deer and goats also contribute to a lesser extent. The impacts of rabbits, mountain hares and voles, which are not discussed here, can be significant in localised areas.

Herbivore impacts on vegetation are the result of a complex set of interactions between the grazer and the grazed vegetation. Herbivores affect vegetation through direct defoliation of selected plant species, and by trampling, dunging, urination and miscellaneous behavioural characteristics such as tree thrashing. Defoliation has the greatest impact on plant growth and productivity. It also affects the reproductive capacity of plants and competitive interactions between plant species. Grazing therefore has a strong influence on species diversity, the relative abundance of plant species and the structure of vegetation.

Defoliation impacts are often widespread and visible at a landscape scale whilst trampling, dunging and behavioural damage generally tend to be more localised. Herbivore impacts on vegetation may be considered to be either beneficial or detrimental depending on the objectives of management.

The pattern and degree of impact of herbivores on plant species and vegetation communities can be very variable and much of this depends on:

- species composition of the vegetation
- season of grazing
- grazing pressure
- type of grazing animal
- site characteristics
- other management factors

Each of these is discussed below.

Species composition of vegetation

Plant species vary widely in their tolerance to herbivore impacts with some being quite resilient and able to survive grazing or browsing for long periods, whilst others are killed rapidly. The variability in plant response and tolerance to direct herbivore impacts and indirectly through the affects on competitive interactions between plant species has a strong influence on the species composition of vegetation.

There are many strategies by which plants avoid selection or react to herbivore impacts and these are largely dependent on certain intrinsic characteristics, such as their morphology or growth form, chemistry, growth rate and life-history. An understanding of these attributes of plant species is useful in predicting the likelihood of selection by a herbivore, and the degree and type of damage the plant will sustain, the chances of survival and the effects on the competitive ability of the affected plant.

A critical part of a plant's growth-form is the position of the growing points (perennating buds). In this respect grazing pressure and timing are crucial factors in determining the impact. Some plants can produce new shoots and leaves from buds which are below grazing level, throughout the growing season. Thus, despite continuous defoliation, such plants are most likely to survive. Typical of these are many tillering species, such as many pasture grasses (bents, fescues and meadow grasses) and some sedges, which are extremely successful in resisting grazing at any time of year.

Woody species, such as trees and many shrubs, are least tolerant of grazing because their growing points and a large part of their food storage area (shoots, evergreen leaves, stems) are exposed to partial or even complete removal. Gymnosperms (for example, Scots pine) are less tolerant of browsing than many broad-leaved trees. Woody species may survive but their growth can be extremely stunted, with flowering and seed production inhibited by removal of fruiting branches.

Morphological adaptations, such as small growth forms which may be less visible to herbivores, are widespread in plant species and can also be induced in response to repeated defoliation. Tall herbs such as globeflower, meadowsweet and hogweed are preferentially selected even at light stocking densities and if the plants survive, they do so with dwarfed leaves. Once grazing pressures are sufficiently relaxed or the timing of grazing is altered, such forms may reach their full stature.

Many plants develop defences to herbivory by the production of secondary chemical compounds which make plants distasteful or less digestible or by the development of morphological characteristics such as stiff hairs and spines. These plants are less likely to be grazed or they may only be selected at certain stages in their life-cycle, when they are more attractive. Mat-grass (Nardus stricta) for example, tends only to be grazed by sheep in the spring when the leaves are young and possibly contain less silica than older leaves.

Plants with rapid growth rates and that recycle nutrients efficiently, particularly if they also produce underground storage organs, are less likely to be susceptible to damage from defoliation. Some bent and fescue grasses with high growth rates respond by rapid production of new and often nutritious (to herbivores) leaves, but others, such as mat-grass and purple moor grass, have low growth rates so that heavy and prolonged defoliation can reduce the vigour of these species.

Most green (vascular) plants go through a life-history which consists of a seedling stage, root and shoot extension, flowering, seed production and senescence. The time-scales over which this cycle occurs ranges from a few weeks for some fast-growing ruderal plants to several hundred years for some trees. Attractiveness and availability to herbivores and vulnerability to damage from herbivore impacts varies during the plant's life-history.

The most vulnerable stage for many plants is that of the seedling, when food reserves are limited and root and shoot development may not be sufficient to maintain nutrient supplies. A seedling grazed or trampled at this stage is likely to perish. Plants with short life-histories usually rely on annual or biennial seed production, gaps in the sward at the right time for germination to occur and rapid growth rates which allows them to out-compete neighbouring species. Plants with longer life-histories such as biennials or perennials, tend to rely on substantial allocation of resources to storage tissues. Herbivore impact may adversely affect this such that general plant vigour is reduced and susceptibility to disease or other damage is increased.

Some plant species, such as wild angelica, are least tolerant of grazing when they are growing most vigorously but tolerate grazing at a later stage in their annual growth cycle. Other species, such as heather, can sustain prolonged grazing whilst the shrub is young and at its most vigorous growth stage. Older age classes of heather may be more severely damaged by grazing and trampling impacts because the ability to regenerate declines with age.

The species composition of vegetation also affects herbivore diet selection. This appears to depend primarily on the relative digestibility of the plant species. In general there is a broad hierarchy of selection of plant species with certain fine-leaved grasses, herbs and sedges being preferred to more coarse-leaved tussock grasses and sedges, rushes, dwarf shrubs and trees, with mosses and lichens least preferred. These choices are however, strongly influenced by other factors such as the the season, the age and condition of individual plant species, the species and breed of herbivore and the range of vegetation types within the herbivore foraging area.

Season of Grazing

Plant species vary in their susceptibility to grazing at different times of year and herbivore preferences for individual species also changes during the year. These factors can be used by graziers and managers to influence the nature of the grazed vegetation.

Seasonality affects plant growth rates and, once established, many plants stand a better chance of recovery if grazed earlier, rather than later in the season when growing conditions are not so favourable and plants are less able to make up lost tissues and storage reserves. Grasses tend to be less adversely affected by grazing than most broad-leaved herbs so grazing when grass growth rates are high, i.e. spring and summer, encourages graminoids at the expense of broad-leaved herb species which are likely to be selected and are very sensitive to grazing impacts in these seasons. Many broad-leaved herbs benefit from late summer, autumn or winter grazing once their main period of active growth and seeding has occurred. This allows their seed to disperse, to accumulate in a seed bank and winter trampling also opens up niches for autumn or spring germination. Grasslands and grassy heaths grazed late in the year can become much richer in broad-leaved plant species and the increased abundance of flowering has beneficial effects for many invertebrate species. Light summer grazing pressures or summer rest for species-rich grassland tends to encourage herb species and results in greater plant diversity within the sward.

Perennial and long-lived plants, especially those which can reproduce vegetatively and whose life-histories generally span several years may not be so affected by seasonal grazing regimes. Their populations and genetic diversity may however, be threatened in the long-term if they are unable to flower and set seed and establish new plants, at least occasionally. In this case, they may respond favourably to intermittent episodes of all-year grazing, or light summer and late season grazing especially if this reduces tussocky grasses and shrubs, breaks up litter and opens up the turf. This is more beneficial than low levels of continuous grazing when palatable perennial herbs may be preferentially selected every year (especially by sheep or red deer).

Timing of grazing is important in its influence on the composition and abundance of species within heath communities. In early autumn sheep will select attractive graminoid species until the biomass is removed and/or the digestibility has declined when sheep will switch to the dwarf shrubs. Heather in mat-grass dominated grassland where palatable graminoids are less abundant, may be selected much earlier. However, light summer grazing on the current years shoots of heather is tolerable since regrowth can restore the lost carbohydrate reserves which will be drawn on in spring. Productivity of heather is more severely affected by autumn and winter removal of shoots during which time grazing pressure is an important factor in the survival of heather shrubs.

Seasonality also affects the nutritional quality of plants in respect to herbivores. The digestibility of plant material generally declines towards the autumn and litter increases, making the sward less attractive to herbivores. This influences the distribution of herbivores and the grazing pressure they exert on the plant species since, although there is variation between species, herbivores generally select the highest quality available plants.

Grazing Pressure

Grazing pressure has a large influence on the structure and species composition of vegetation, due to the differences between plants in tolerance to herbivore impacts and the knock-on effect on competitive interactions between plants. Very generally, on grazed swards as pressures increase, utilisation rates (the proportion of annual productivity of plants removed by grazing) are higher, swards become more uniform and species-richness increases up to a point. Very heavily grazed grasslands can become dominated by a few bryophytes and species-richness may decline.

When grazing pressures and utilisation rates are low the sward structure is more varied but species-richness may be reduced by the dominance of a few, more competitively aggressive plant species. Where grazing and browsing pressure is maintained over long periods this tends to result in grazing-tolerant assemblages of plants often dominated by graminoid species. Woodlands in which grazing pressures are low may also become very species-rich.

In free-ranging situations, grazing pressure and therefore utilisation rates are influenced by the quality of the available forage. Utilisation rates will always be highest on the most preferred plant species and types of vegetation. As herbivore densities increase or herbage quality (cf. seasonal effects) or quantity declines, the amount of plant material per animal reduces. In these situation utilisation rates increase,

selection becomes less discriminating and less preferred plant species will then be grazed.

Utilisation rates can be useful in predicting the potential changes to vegetation with variation in grazing pressure. For example, grasslands dominated by bents and fescues can probably remain fairly stable at 60-70% utilisation of the leafy material. It is known experimentally that vigorous young heather on dry heaths, can sustain a utilisation rate of up to 40% of the current season's shoot productivity but above 80% utilisation, heather bushes are out-competed by grasses and decline in cover. Sustainable utilisation rates also depend on local site conditions (altitude, climate, exposure, soil nutrient status) and these factors must be taken into account when estimating productivity and thresholds of sustainable utilisation. For example, heather growing in blanket bog where productivity is hampered by high water tables, may only maintain cover at utilisation rates of less than 15% of the current season's shoot growth.

A change in grazing pressure, if maintained, will eventually result in successional change to the vegetation. For example, prolonged and heavy grazing pressures in autumn and winter on heather can reduce its productivity to the extent that competitive species of grasses and sedges come to replace the heather. Reductions in grazing pressure will permit regeneration of heather when some bushes remain, and in the long-term colonisation by trees may occur if grazing pressure continues to be low enough.

Crude predictions of species abundance and composition and likely trends of change in vegetation communities are possible to forecast, although the time-scales over which the changes occur are very variable. Factors such as the site characteristics and the initial composition of the vegetation at the time of alteration in grazing pressure are important influences on the type of subsequent vegetation community and the direction of successional change.

Types of Grazing Animal

Different species and breeds of herbivore differ in their grazing behaviour and have different impacts on plant species. Selection of plant species is quite variable both within and between animal species. Primitive breeds such as Hebridean sheep for example, on heather moors, will select mat grass and purple moor-grass and encourage heather. The reverse is the case with most commercial hill ewe breeds although hill wethers are reputed to have similar preferences for rough grasses.

Different animal species can also have pronounced effects on species composition, sward heights and structure through differential plant selection, trampling and dunging patterns. For example, cattle (and goats) will tend to graze taller vegetation and leave an uneven tussocky swards (useful for ground nesting birds). Cattle can produce a very short sward, although possibly at a cost to their body condition. With their heavy body weight, cattle can knock down tall vegetation, open up thick turf through trampling and provide germination sites for other plant species. However, on very wet soils, cattle trampling impacts can be damaging to soil structure and plants. Cattle dung may smother plants and they also avoid grazing dunged patches for some time, resulting in patches of tall vegetation.

At moderate to high grazing pressures sheep, red deer and horses tend to graze closely and leave a short sward of even height whilst at low grazing pressures, the sward will be more varied in structure. Trampling impacts by sheep tend to be fairly light, except on bare ground or light soils, but sheep can initiate or exacerbate erosive processes by making 'scrapes' and

lying up in peat hags for shelter. Certain plants such as Sphagna in bogs and lichen on heaths may be damaged by even light sheep and deer trampling. During the day, sheep dung where they graze, but at night they tend to lie up and dunging can become more concentrated.

Ponies and horses are not ruminants and therefore they feed for much longer periods than other herbivores. They can strongly affect species composition since they can graze as close as rabbits and are as selective, preferring grasses but also taking sedges and rushes. Equines apparently avoid a number of flowering plants but they may also entirely eliminate certain plant species. At low enough pressures, they can leave a very varied structure of sward with patches close-grazed and tussocky ground. Equines tend to dung in latrines, and species composition in these areas can be profoundly affected.

The nutrients in dung and urine are in a readily available form for uptake by plants. In nutrient poor habitats, such as blanket bogs, there may be significant nutrient enrichment through increased availability of potential nitrogen and potassium. This may affect species competitiveness and favour other plant species. Dung also contains seeds, so 'alien' species, perhaps from supplementary feeding of domestic stock, may be transferred between communities. The effects can be especially concentrated where stock shelter, rest up or where supplementary feeding occurs and sometimes results in undesirable species assemblages such as rank grasses, docks, nettles and thistles.

Site characteristics

The characteristics of a site have profound influences the species composition and distribution of different vegetation types depending on the topography, climate, geology, soil types and drainage pattern.

High altitude and exposed areas of sites are more likely to support climax vegetation types, not necessarily very attractive to herbivores except in summer. Prolonged grazing pressure of sufficient intensity can however, alter certain climax communities. Alpine moss-heaths for example, can lose the moss component through trampling damage and move towards grazing-tolerant grass-dominated communities instead.

Lower altitude valley slopes which might have remnant tree and tall herb species confined to ledges, tend to support plagioclimax vegetation types such as dry dwarf shrub habitats and grasslands. It is these areas that have the greatest potential for relatively rapid successional vegetation change depending on local conditions. Blanket bog tends to be intermediate in potential for change depending on the nature of the bog, the site character-istics and past management practices.

Where alterations in herbivore management with consequent changes in grazing pressure are proposed, site factors must be considered in the prediction of likely changes to vegetation both in respect of their influence on the plant species and in the distribution of herbivores. For example, high altitude vegetation may be quite sensitive to even low grazing pressures especially where plant growth is limited by a short growing season, temperature extremes and the substrate is unstable. Trampling and dunging rather than direct defoliation may have a greater impact, especially on slow growing or fragile species such as bryophytes or lichens. Sheltered areas of a site such as corries, or woodland are always likely to be well used by herbivores and although the herbivore population may be reduced overall on a site, such areas may still attract similar densities at certain times of year. Cliffs, ravines and gullies are often important refuges for grazing-sensitive plant species. Along with water bodies such features can also act as natural barriers to herbivore movement and may be used to influence siting of fences to control ranging behaviour.

Other Management Factors

Moor gripping (shallow surface draining) of blanket bog and burning of bog and heaths have profound impacts on upland plant communities. Burning is designed to benefit grouse, deer or sheep by favouring the production of young and more nutritious stands of heather. The ultimate aim of moor gripping is to promote a greater abundance of palatable grassland species and increase the heather component by drying out the bog surface.

If management is poor both practices can be detrimental to the above aims. Post-burn plant succession is affected by the original species composition, the timing of the burn in relation to the life-history of those species and the intensity of the burn. The more intense the burn, the longer the likely period of regeneration due to removal of all stems which have basal shoots from which regrowth occurs, loss of the seed bank and potential destabili-sation of the substrate. The scale and spatial arrangement of burnt patches also influences distribution of herbivores. Small burn patches amongst extensive unburnt areas tend to attract high grazing pressures and this will also delay regeneration of dwarf shrub species.

Frequency of burning also has an important influence on species composition. Where burning has been too frequent on wetter moors (e.g. north-west Highlands) purple moor grass or cotton grass gains a competitive advantage over heather resulting in dominance of the vegetation by plant species which have virtually no feeding value in winter and are only eaten in large quantities by cattle and certain sheep breeds in summer.

Moor gripping can also initiate or speed up erosive processes in the bog surface resulting in a network of wet unvegetated channels and dry heather dominated ridges which have limited value for grazing animals.

Summary

Grazing plays a large part in determining the composition of upland plant communities and the interaction of the factors outlined above leads to enhancement, maintenance or loss of plant species. By managing the grazing pressure, timing and selectivity (by area or species) of grazing, plant species composition can be influenced.

Historically, the Scottish Uplands have always been grazed and the plant communities found there are maintained by, or are tolerant of grazing to some degree. A practical and informed approach to grazing management will contribute to the maintenance of these plant communities in optimal condition.

Author:
Sarah Eno.

Acknowledgements:
Roy A. Harris, J. Milne, D. Welch, J. Fenton and Helen Armstrong for useful comments.

Further reading and information:

The bibliography lists a number of conservation manuals published by the RSPB etc. where the use of grazing for particular purposes is described. None of these refer specifically to the less well known but important upland habitats.

MacDonald *et al.* (1998). *A Guide to Upland Habitats: Surveying Land Management Impacts.* Scottish Natural Heritage. Battleby, Perth. Grazing impacts on upland vegetation communities in Scotland is extensively discussed.

Harris, R.A. & Jones, R.M. (in press) *Loft & Hill of White Hamars Grazing Project: Management Advisory Note 1.* Available from Loft, Longhope, South Walls, Hoy, Orkney KW16 3PQ.

See also in this manual:
Appendix 6 *The Grazing Behaviour of Large Herbivores in the Uplands.*

Appendix 11 *Computer-based Decision Support Tools available to Aid Grazing Management.*

APPENDIX 13

Agricultural Support and Environmental Incentives

This section summarises environmental grants and agricultural subsidies available in the Scottish uplands. Amounts payable are not included since they quickly become outdated.

Agricultural Support

This section summarises agricultural support available for livestock, through the European Union's (EU) Common Agricultural Policy.

Hill Livestock Compensatory Allowances (HLCA)

Administered by SOAEFD, the allowance is paid annually on the number of breeding cows and ewes on holdings in Less Favoured Areas (LFAs). The scheme aims to encourage farming in disadvantaged areas. To qualify for LFA status the land must have been accepted by SOAEFD as being suitable for extensive livestock production. LFAs are further divided into Severely Disadvantaged Areas (SDA) and Disadvantaged Areas (DA). Within the Highlands and Islands Enterprise Area rates of payment are higher for SDAs.

Payments are limited by stocking density, for sheep this is limited to a maximum of 6 ewes per hectare in SDAs and 9 ewes per hectare in DAs. Allowances are also limited to 1.4 Livestock Units (LUs) per forage hectare for each holding. For this purpose 1 LU = 1 cow or 6 2/3 ewes. These rates are above normal agricultural stocking rates and so tend not to restrict numbers in practice. Penalties for overgrazing are in existence whereby the allowance can be withheld if the condition of the natural vegetation is deteriorating.

Sheep Annual Premium Scheme (SAPS)

This is a market support mechanism designed to make up any deficiency in the market price for lamb when compared to the annual support price set annually by the EU.

Payments of SAP are controlled by means of a quota system limiting the numbers of sheep on which payment will be paid. Payment is based on the number of female sheep that, by the last day of a specified retention period, have either given birth to a lamb or have attained the age of 12 months .

The SAP is not subject to a stocking rate limit thus allowing farm income to increase exponentially with the number of ewes. In practise this encourages intensive stocking of sheep in the uplands. For example in 1996 for an upland farm of 1000 ha in an LFA with quota for 4000 sheep the annual sheep subsidy would have been £100,000. Also if the quota is being fulfilled there is little incentive to minimise lamb mortality rates and attention to animal welfare especially during the lambing season may be reduced.

Penalties for overgrazing exist within the scheme if the natural vegetation is in poor condition.

Beef Special Premium Scheme (BSPS)

The premium is only applicable to male cattle and can be claimed twice in the animals lifetime; firstly when it is aged between 10 and 23 months and secondly when it is over 23 months. Claims can only be made on the first 90 animals in each group. To qualify for payment a stocking rate of 2 LUs per hectare must not be exceeded. Penalties for overgrazing exist within the scheme if the natural vegetation is in poor condition.

Under this scheme documentation of cattle movements must be kept , compensation for losses made due to the Bovine Spongiform Encephalopathy (BSE) crisis have been made under this scheme.

Suckler Cow Premium Scheme (SCPS)

This scheme operates in a similar manner to the SAP scheme. It is limited by quotas based on the holdings beef production in 1992 and is limited by a maximum stocking rate of 2 beef cows per hectare. This stocking rate does not exclude other types of cattle on which premium is not being claimed. Compensation for losses made due to the BSE crisis have been made under this scheme.

Extensification Premium

This additional payment can be claimed in addition to SCP and BSP if the stocking rate is less than 1.4 LUs per hectare. The stocking rate is calculated from the number of beasts for which the farmer claims any of the above listed premia.

There are several additional livestock-related schemes mainly developed in response to the BSE crisis. Agri-Environment Programme (AEP) The Scottish AEP is currently (1997) composed of three parts - the Countryside Premium Scheme (CPS); the Environmentally Sensitive Areas Scheme (EASs), and the Organic Aid Scheme (OAS). The Heather Moorland Scheme, Habitats Scheme and Set-Aside Access Scheme have been integrated into CPS and are therefore no longer available separately.

Countryside Premium Scheme

This is a voluntary scheme administered by The Scottish Office Agriculture, Environment and Fisheries Department (SOAEFD). Payments are provided for a range of management and capital options (Table 1) which are designed to encourage environmentally friendly farming. If payment is received from the scheme then habitats must be managed in accordance with chosen management options and the land manager must adhere to certain environmental conditions over the whole of their land.

The scheme is open to farmers and crofters outside existing Environmentally Sensitive Areas (ESA's). A conservation audit listing habitats and features with an assessment of their current conservation status must be submitted with the application. If the scheme is oversubscribed then locally agreed priority options will take precedence.

TABLE 1: Habitat management and creation and capital options available in the Scottish uplands

Management and Creation Options	Capital Options
Management of silage / hay fields for birds Management of species-rich grassland Creation of species-rich grassland Management of wetland Creation of wetland Management of water margins Management of coastal heath Management of moorland - stock disposal * Management of moorland - muirburn Creation of grass margins or beetlebanks Creation of conservation headlands Creation of extended hedges Management of scrub Management of archaeological/historic sites Provision of access	Bracken control Fences, gates, stiles and footbridges Water troughs Sowing of species-rich grassland Drystone dykes Vernacular building restoration Tree planting Planting / managing hedges Creation or restoration of ponds

* Must be accompanied by a moorland management plan which reports on the condition of the existing moor and proposes management changes.

Environmentally Sensitive Areas (ESAs)

There are 10 ESAs in Scotland amounting to 19% of the land area. Of these, eight are in upland areas; Western Southern Uplands, Stewartry, Breadalbane and Loch Lomond, Argyll Islands, Shetland Islands, Central Southern Uplands, Central Borders and Cairngorm Straths. The scheme is administered by SOAEFD.

ESAs were originally introduced under the 1986 Agriculture Act to help conserve areas of high landscape, historic or wildlife value which are vulnerable to changes in agricultural practices.

Entry into the scheme is on a voluntary basis, but farmers and crofters who join are required to continue with or agree to specific farming measures which help protect and enhance conservation value on their land. The land is farmed under a ten year agreement with a 5 year opt-out clause. Payments are available within three broad categories ;

- payments per hectare for all areas covered by standard environmental requirements within the scheme whereby farmers or crofters adopt environmentally friendly farming methods.

- payments for specific management measures on areas of high conservation value (Table 2).

- payments for specific conservation improvements e.g. fencing , erection of gates, and tree planting.

Applications must be accompanied by a farm conservation plan outlining all conservation features with proposals for appropriate management.

TABLE 2: Payments available to enhance or extend areas of land or features with a high conservation value
(* denotes payment available).

Management measures to enhance and extend existing features	ENVIRONMENTALLY SENSITIVE AREAS							
	Cairngorm Straths	Central Borders	Central Southern Uplands	Shetland	Argyll	Breadalbane /Loch omond	Stewartry	West Southern Uplands
Native/amenity woodland/scrub	*	*	*	*	*	*	*	*
Herb-rich unimproved grassland	*	*	*	*	*	*	*	*
Arable cropping	*			*	*			
Winter keep production	*							
Water margins	*	*	*			*	*	*
Heathland regeneration;	*		*	*	*	*	*	*
- muirburn	*		*	*	*	*	*	*
- stock management	*		*	*	*	*	*	*
- stock reduction	*		*	*	*	*	*	*
Archaeological sites	*	*	*	*	*	*	*	*
Wetland/catchment areas		*						*
Extending hedgerows		*	*				*	
Grassland bird measures				*	*			
Dunes/Machair management					*			

Organic Aid Scheme

This was launched in June 1994. It provides assistance for crofters and farmers who wish to convert to organic farming. To receive aid, farmers and crofters must meet the farming standards set by United Kingdom Register of Organic Food Standards (UKROFS), which provides guidance for the care of the environment. Farmers and crofters enter into a binding agreement to convert all or part of their holding to organic standards. They will be eligible for an annual payment on each hectare entered for a five year period plus an additional payment per hectare for the first 5 ha entered.

Scottish Natural Heritage (SNH) environmental grants

Grants are available to land managers, farmers, and crofters to improve the wildlife value and appearance of their land through;
- the creation or enhancement of habitats such as native woodlands, old hay meadows, wetland, herb-rich grasslands, heather moorland, peatlands, riverbanks and ponds.

- the improvement or creation of landscape features such as hedgerows, woodlands and historic features.

- the conservation or enhancement of geological features

- measures to conserve species e.g. the provision of nest boxes

Grants are also available to assist land managers with public access and recreation through;
- access provision e.g. footpath creation and management, sign-posting and waymarking

- recreational provisions such as visitor centres and interpretative facilities

- the provision of a ranger service

SNH also provide grants for the production of whole farm or estate management plans. Priority will be given to proposals on designated areas such as Special Areas of Conservation and Sites of Special Scientific Interest.

Woodland Grants
Woodland Grant Scheme (WGS)
Administered by the Forestry Authority (FA) grants are available to:
- encourage the creation of new woodlands and forests which benefit wildlife, improve the landscape, increase the production of wood and offer opportunities for recreation and sport.

- encourage good woodland and forest management especially for natural regeneration and within ancient and semi-natural woodlands.

- to provide jobs and improve the economy of rural areas and other areas with few other sources of economic activity

- to provide a use for land other than agricultural

Small and very narrow areas of woodland (less than .25ha in area or 15m wide) may not be eligible to enter the scheme.

Payments are on a per hectare basis and a higher rate is available for new planting on arable or improved grassland.

Natural regeneration
Payments are also on a per hectare basis for restocking or natural regeneration. To qualify for a grant to encourage natural regeneration stocking rates of cattle and or sheep must be reduced to an appropriate level. Funds may also be available to assist with the works required to encourage natural regeneration.

Annual Management Grant
An annual payment to contribute towards the cost of managing woodlands for conservation, landscape or recreation is available.

Woodland Improvement Grant (WIG)

There are three WIG projects: 1. Providing public recreation in woodlands, 2. Undermanaged Woods (bringing woodlands which are undermanaged or of low commercial value, back into management and, 3. Woodland Biodiversity (work which aid the forestry aspects of the UK Biodiversity Action Plan).

The grant is a single payment to cover half the net cost of suitable work up to a limit of £10,000. Challenge funds may also be available under 2 and 3.

Livestock Exclusion Annual Premium

A per hectare payment to encourage the removal of sheep and cattle from woodlands. The payment lasts for up to 10 years and aims to compensate the farmer for loss of income.

Farm Woodland Premium Scheme (FWPS)

The scheme is administered jointly by the FA and SOAEFD. It aims to encourage tree planting on land that has been in recent agricultural use e.g. livestock farming and arable cropping. Annual payments are made over 15 years for woodlands containing more than 50% per area of broadleaved trees and over 10 years for woodlands containing 50% or more per area of coniferous trees. There is an upper limit of 200ha per farm business and planting on unimproved land must not

exceed 40ha. This scheme is also available to crofters for common grazings but planting must not exceed 100ha per common grazings area. Payment is in addition to the establishment grants available under the Woodland Grant Scheme.

Objective 1 Highlands & Islands Agricultural Programme

Agricultural Business Improvement Scheme (ABIS)

This scheme is administered by SOAEFD. Grants are aimed at improving the efficiency of agricultural businesses within the Objective 1 area. Queries on whether a unit is within the Objective 1 area should be addressed to SOAEFD. Funds are also available for measures which have an environmental benefit (Table 3). The scheme is open to farmers, crofters, partnerships, companies and other legal occupiers of land who are carrying out an eligible agricultural business within the area.

Prerequisites for entry into the scheme are a resource audit and business assessment which is grant aided at 50% up to a maximum amount.

Crofting Township Development Scheme

Aimed at encouraging sustainable agricultural development whilst adopting environmentally beneficial measures. Projects should be of a social or cultural nature.

The scheme is administered by the Crofters Commission on behalf of SOAEFD.

Crofting Counties Agricultural Grant Scheme (CCAGS)

Available to crofters and eligible land managers in the former crofting counties of Argyll, Ross and Cromarty, Sutherland, Caithness, Orkney and Shetland. Grant aided works include: bracken control, planting shelterbelts and provision of hedges and dykes. The scheme is administered by the Crofters Commission.

TABLE 3: ABIS Environmental measures
Environmental Enhancement Measures
Stone dyke restoration
Fencing for conservation management
Shelterbelt and amenity tree planting
Eradication of bracken
Heather regeneration
Rhododendron control
Pond restoration
Creation of wetlands and marshlands
Planting of approved species to encourage wildlife habitats

Objective 5b: Rural Diversification Programme (RDP)

This operates in four designated areas of Scotland: Borders, Dumfries & Galloway, North and West Grampian, Rural Stirling and Upland Tayside. The main aim is to provide assistance to people actively engaged in agriculture towards the establishment of new economic enterprises or to support expansion of existing suitable enterprises. Contact SOAEFD, SNH or local authority.

Local Grant Schemes

Local grants may be available from some local authorities e.g. East and North Grampian Conservation Projects or other organisations such as the Royal Society for the Protection of Birds. Information on these should be requested locally.

TABLE 4: Summary table showing availability of main environmental grants and incentives. *denotes payment available*

Eligible Works	CPS	ESAs	SNH	WGS & WIGS	HIE Agri-Programme	CCAGS
	ENVIRONMENTAL GRANTS					
Management of silage / hay fields for birds	*	*	*			
Management of species-rich grassland	*	*	*			
Creation of species-rich grassland	*	*	*			
Management of wetland	*	*	*			
Creation of wetland	*	*	*		*	*
Management of water margins	*	*	*			
Management of coastal heath	*	*	*			
Management of moorland - stock disposal *	*	*	*			
Management of moorland - muirburn	*	*	*			
Creation of grass margins or beetlebanks	*	*	*			
Creation of conservation headlands	*	*	*			
Creation of extended hedges	*	*	*		*	*
Management of scrub	*	*	*	*		*
Management of archaeological/historic sites	*	*	*			
Provision of access	*		*	*		
Tree planting	*	*	*	*	*	*
Woodland Management	*	*	*	*		
Stone dyking	*	*	*		*	*
Rhododendron control			*		*	*
Bracken control					*	*

Author:
Kath Lee

Acknowledgements:
Daniel Gotts

Contact Addresses:

Crofters Commission
4/6 Castle Wynde,
Inverness, IV2 3EQ
Tel: 01463 663450

Scottish Natural Heritage
12 Hope Terrace
Edinburgh EH9 2AS
Tel: 0131 447 4784

Forestry Authority,
231 Corstorphine Road,
Edinburgh EH12 7AT
Tel: 0131 334 0303

Scottish Office Agricultural Environment
and Fisheries Department
Pentland House
47 Robb's Loan
Edinburgh EH14 1TW
Tel: 0131 556 8400

Historic Scotland
20 Brandon Street
Edinburgh EH3 5RA
Tel: 0131 244 3107

REFERENCES

COUNTRYSIDE COUNCIL FOR WALES (1996). *A Guide to the Production of Management Plans for Nature Reserves and Protected Areas.* Countryside Council for Wales.

JERRAM, R. &. DREWITT, A. (1998). *Assessing Vegetation Condition in the Uplands.* English Nature Research Reports Number 264. ISSN 0967-876X

MACDONALD, A., STEVENS, A., ARMSTRONG, H., IMMIRZI, P., & REYNOLDS, P. (1998). *A Guide to Upland Habitats: Surveying Land Management Impacts.* Scottish Natural Heritage. Battleby, Perth.

MLURI (1982) *Soil Survey of Scotland.* Macaulay Land Use Research Institute, Aberdeen.

NATURE CONSERVANCY COUNCIL (1988). *Site Management Plans for Nature Conservation.* Nature Conservancy Council Publicity Services Branch. ISBN 0 86139 414 3

RATCLIFFE, D., (1977) *The Nature Conservation Review.* Cambridge University Press

RODWELL, J.S. ed. (1991). *British Plant Communities, Volume 1, Woodlands and Scrub.* Cambridge University Press. ISBN 0 521 39165 2

RODWELL, J.S. ed. (1991a). *British Plant Communities, Volume 2, Mires and Heaths.* Cambridge University Press. ISBN 0 521 23558 8

RODWELL, J.S. ed. (1992b). *British Plant Communities, Volume 3, Grasslands and Montane Communities.* Cambridge University Press. ISBN 0 521 39166 0

RODWELL, J.S. ed. (1995). *British Plant Communities, Volume 4, Aquatic Communities, Swamps and Tall Herb Fens.* Cambridge University Press. ISBN 0 521 39168 7

Further Reading:

ANDREWS, J., REBANE, M., (1994). *Farming and Wildlife. A Practical Management Handbook.* RSPB 375/94.

BACKSHALL, J., & MANLEY, V.G., (1998). *The Upland Management Handbook.* English Nature, Peterborough.

ENGLISH NATURE (1996). *Land Management for Upland Birds.* English Nature.

ENGLISH NATURE (1997). *Enact. Managing Land for Wildlife. Vol 5 No. 4.* English Nature, Peterborough

FULLER, R.J. (1996). *Relationships Between Grazing and Birds with Particular Reference to sheep in the British Uplands. British Trust for Ornithology.* BTO Research Report No 164.

Interpretation Manual of European Habitats - EUR 12 1995/2. DGXI, European Commission, Directorate General XI, Rue de la Loi, B1049 Brussels.

JNCC (1992) *Guidelines to the selection of biological Sites of Special Scientific Interest.* Publications Branch, JNCC, Monkstone House, City Road, Peterborough, PE1 1JY

MILNE, J.A., BIRCH, C.P.D., HESTER, A.J., ARMSTRONG, H.M., AND ROBERTSON, A. (In Press) *Impacts of Vertebrate Herbivores on the Natural Heritage of the Scottish Uplands - a Review.* Scottish Natural Heritage Review No. 95, Battleby.

RSPB, THE SCOTTISH OFFICE AND SCOTTISH AGRICULTURAL COLLEGE. *A Management Guide to Birds of Scottish Farmland.* RSPB 78/1002/96.

SUTHERLAND, W.J., HILL, D.A. (ed) (1995). *Managing Habitats for Conservation.* Cambridge University Press.

WYATT, B.K., GREATOREX-DAVIES, N., BUNCE, R.G.H., FULLER, R.M., HILL., M.O., (1993) *Comparisons of Land Cover. A Dictionary of surveys and classifications of land cover and land use.* Eastcote, Department of the Environment.

SNH Information & Advisory Notes:

The full list of SNH Information and Advisory Notes is available from SNH Publications, Battleby, Redgorton, Perth, Scotland PH1 3EW. Those most relevant to this manual are:

ARMSTRONG, H. *The Grazing Behaviour of Large Herbivores in the Uplands.* SNH I & A note No.47 (also included as an appendix in this manual)

FLEMING, V. & SYDES, C. *Priority Species in Scotland: Plants.* SNH I & A Note No.48

GOTTS, D. *Grazing Management - Unimproved and Herb Rich Pasture.* SNH I & A Note No.8

MACDONALD, A. & ANDREWS, J. *Fences and Upland Conservation Management.* SNH I & A Note No.59

PHILLIPS, D. & COOPER, M. *Priority Species in Scotland: Animals.* SNH I & A Note No.49

ROBERTS, J., WOOD-GEE, V. *Drystane Dykes and Stone Fanks.* SNH I & A Note No.25

THOMSON, D. & RINNING, A. *Deer (Scotland) Act 1996; Guidance for SNH Staff.* SNH I & A Note No.94.